COMEBACK

COMEBACK

The Story of My Stroke

ROBERT E. VAN ROSEN

as told to Kendell Crossen

 THE **BOBBS-MERRILL** COMPANY, INC.
A SUBSIDIARY OF HOWARD W. SAMS & CO., INC.
Publishers • INDIANAPOLIS • NEW YORK

Library of Congress Catalog card Number 62-19312

To Marcia, my wife

ACKNOWLEDGMENTS

It is impossible to write a book like this without being indebted to many persons. I am deeply grateful to my wife, Marcia, my sisters, Beatrice, Ahda, and Rhyissa and my daughter Elissa, for their constant encouragement and help from the time when the book was only an idea. I cannot adequately express my thanks to Dr. Zofia Laszewski and her entire staff, including Nathan Melniker, Mrs. Eleanor B. Morrison, Mrs. Shirley Jackson, Dr. Jane Dorsey Zimmerman, Mrs. Sally G. Flynn, Dr. Manuel Riklan, and Mrs. Elton. Dr. Doris T. Leberfeld and Mrs. Joyce Buck, at the Speech and Hearing Center of Hunter College of the City University of New York, were extremely helpful. I also want to thank Dr. Montague Ullman, Mrs. Fitzgerald of the Polyclinic Hospital, and Peter Magazu of the Albany Medical College. And finally I want to add strong personal thanks to my physician, who prefers to remain anonymous, for making this book possible by saving my life when I had the stroke.

R.E.V.R.

Contents

COMEBACK

Preface

It was a beautiful spring day in June, 1959. My wife and I were going to visit friends in Connecticut. Three weeks earlier I'd had a complete physical examination and had been told that I was in perfect condition. I was fifty-five years old and in good health. I had a lovely young wife and we were going to the country to visit good friends. It was spring—the time of the renewal of life. Everything was perfect—except for one thing. I was an established packaging consultant and had been for five years. I had recently started a new phase of my business, selling my services on a subscription basis. Many companies had been interested but only one company had taken a full subscription and one had subscribed for half a year. It meant that I had to keep the business operating but that it wouldn't pay for itself immediately. I had been worried and irritated by the situation and welcomed the idea of a holiday out of the city.

My wife and I left New York City early in the morning and were soon in Connecticut. Our friends had a boat and we went out on the Sound immediately upon our arrival. During the morning I had been aware of a strange feeling in my right arm, a vague numbness, but I soon forgot about it.

Lunch was one of my favorites. It was lobster, the rich, succulent meat washed down by good wine. But, suddenly, my right arm refused to function properly and my wife had to help me separate the lobster from its shell. It was awkward and embarrassing but we thought nothing more of it. In fact, I remember that we joked about it.

Late in the afternoon we docked the boat and went to our friends' house. My right arm was still bothering me and my wife again had to help me during dinner, but there was no special discomfort and I was enjoying myself. We stayed fairly late, finally leaving in time to get us home by midnight. On the way my arm seemed to get worse and I noticed a slight thickening of my speech.

For the first time, I was worried. When we reached home I discussed it with my wife, then with one of my sisters by phone, and finally called my doctor. By this time it was well after midnight and he wanted to know if it couldn't wait until morning. I told him that I knew I could talk at the moment but I wasn't sure I'd be able to the following day. He agreed to come, but when I tried to tell him the address I couldn't give the right number and my wife had to give it to him.

It took him only a few minutes to reach our apartment. He examined me and said he thought I'd had a stroke. Within the hour I was admitted to the hospital. At first, my right arm was weak but I was mentally clear and fully conscious although I couldn't read and I had trouble with addresses and telephone numbers. Tests were started immediately to determine whether my stroke had been caused by a clot, a hemorrhage or a tumor. In the meantime, my doctor was concerned enough to order nurses around the clock for me.

Three days later, while they were still testing, I may have had a second stroke, for my condition became worse. My right side was paralyzed, my face was twisted and I was unable to talk. There was a question of whether I would survive; and if I did there was still the paralysis and the inability to talk.

It was a shock; mine had always been an active life. What would it be like to start all over again at the age of fifty-five?

I was born in Kiev, Russia, in 1904. One of my ancestors had been among the three hundred men brought from Holland by Peter the Great to build his ships. At the end of their contract they had been offered Russian citizenship and my family had been among those who stayed.

My father was a successful businessman. He and my uncle manufactured wallpaper and various housing supplies and were construction contractors. For example, when there was a big fair in Kiev they built about one-third of all the special buildings for it. Our family consisted of my mother and father, an aunt, my three sisters,

Beatrice, Ahda and Rhyissa, and myself. Also living in the house were a governess, a nanny, and a maid. There was a seamstress who came each year and stayed about six months while she made new clothes for my mother and sisters. And there was a cook. So you see, we lived comfortably.

With the Revolution most of my father's bank accounts, even those in Switzerland, were seized by the new government. We managed, however, by selling various possessions, and our situation did not change too radically during the Kerensky regime or in the early days of the Bolsheviks.

In the meantime, I had become a member of the Boy Scouts. I was fifteen years old but looked older; within a year I was assistant to the man who was the head of the Scout movement for four or five states, including about three hundred Scoutmasters. He was soon arrested by the secret police and I automatically became the acting head of the Scouts with no one inquiring about my age.

The Boy Scouts in Russia, although a part of the international movement, was quite different from the kind of organization in America. Its training had always had more of a military tinge, and when the Communists took over they kept this in mind. It was a period in which the Bolsheviks were thinking of two objectives concerning the Scouts. They were thinking of changing the name to Young Communists or something that might be translated as Young Trail-Blazers. They were also trying to make rapid changes in the Red Army, since many of the officers were from the Czarist army and they wanted to replace them with young men who had not been trained in the old regime. This was to bring about great changes in the Scouts—and in my life.

The government soon decreed that all Scoutmasters were to be taken into the Red Army and given three months' training, at the end of which time they would become captains. Since I was in charge of the Scoutmasters, I was told that I would be immediately commissioned as a captain without the three months' training. And I was.

The Russian-Polish war was going on then and I was sent to the front almost at once. Fatalities were high among the officers and by the time I was seventeen I had received field promotions to the rank of colonel. The war was over by then and I was sent home as the officer in charge of the Kiev Labor Regiment. Despite its name, this was still the Red Army and our duty was primarily police action in relation to entrances and exits to and from Kiev.

There was still an active underground in Russia, composed of all the various anti-Communist factions who were cooperating regardless of their many differences. Their main objective at the time was the assassination of Lenin; several attempts had already been made, starting in 1918. I was a part of that underground, having joined at about the same time I became a member of the Red Army.

The underground had decided to make a special effort to get Lenin. Carefully selected agents from every area of Russia were to be sent to Moscow in the hope that some would get through. Four were being sent from Kiev. They had to be provided with travel papers since no one could travel in Russia without them. Such papers had to be stamped with an official seal—the only one in the area was in the possession of the political commissar —then signed by the commissar and myself.

I spent an evening with the commissar and saw to it that he had more vodka than he could handle. When he was sodden with drink, I took the seal from his pocket and stamped the papers. I returned the seal to his pocket and signed the papers with his name and mine. Our four agents went off to Moscow—but were caught as soon as they arrived.

At that time the secret police of Russia was the *Chrezvychainaya Komissiya* (its full title was "Extraordinary Commission for Combating Counterrevolution, Sabotage and Speculation")—but to everyone it was known as the Cheka. Moscow, upon the arrest of our four agents, sent word to the Cheka office in Kiev ordering the arrest of the two men who had signed the travel papers.

I did not, of course, know what had happened at that time. I was in my office when I received a phone call from the commissar in charge of arrests of the Kiev Cheka. We had been schoolmates only a few years earlier. He said that he wanted to see me but would prefer we meet at my home as soon as possible. I sensed something serious and agreed.

When we met in my father's house he told me that the four agents had been caught in Moscow and that he had orders to arrest the commissar and myself. There was only one thing he could do, he told me. He could hold up action for about four hours. Then he would have to send his men out to arrest me. "Will you give me your word," he asked, "that you will leave Russia?"

There was little choice. I told him I would. We shook hands and he left.

The first problem was that of my parents and sisters. Once I had escaped, they would be in danger. We held a family conference and decided that they would go to an aunt's house in another part of Kiev. Her surname was different and chances were good that the Cheka wouldn't look for them there.

As soon as they left, I went to the Commissariat (something like the War Ministry), showed my military papers, and explained that my mother was ill in Odessa. I requested permission to go there at once. Since I was in charge of the regiment, and only the Cheka knew about the orders from Moscow, my request was granted. I boarded the next train for Odessa.

It is about six hundred miles from Kiev to Odessa. At that time the train trip took an entire day, so by the time I reached Odessa I knew that every Cheka office would have a description of me and orders for my arrest. I would have to leave the train somewhere before the end of the line.

The train cut straight across Russia for about 250 miles until it was near the border, then turned south and ran along the river down to Odessa. There, I found an opportunity to drop off as it slowed down. I waited by the road until a peasant came along with a horse and cart. I showed him my revolver and told him that I was going to hide in his cart while he drove me to the river separating Russia and Rumania. If he gave me away I would kill him, I warned.

At the river it did not take me long to locate a man who helped people get across the river—for a price. I went to his house and told him that I needed a boat to go over to Rumania. He wanted to know if I had any money. I had a few rubles and a watch which I said I'd give him. I also showed him my revolver and told him that he and I would stay together in the cellar of his house while his wife made the arrangements. He had no choice but to agree.

When I finally got the boat it turned out to be hardly more than a box in which I could crouch while I propelled it across the river with a pole. It wasn't a very good buy but I launched it and began to pole my way to freedom. Halfway across the river I realized it was a worse buy than I'd thought, for it began to sink. I have since suspected this was planned, but at the time I didn't bother with much thinking. I managed to get my clothes off and tie them on top of my head, and started swimming just as the boat went under.

When I reached the Rumanian side I was exhausted. I crawled a few feet up on the beach and went to sleep. I don't know how long I slept but I was awakened by the sound of a shot and a bullet plowing into the sand near me. A Rumanian guard stood a few feet away, his rifle leveled at me.

I signaled with my hands to indicate that I was alive and got slowly to my feet as he came nearer. He permitted me to dress and then I went with him. I was questioned by Rumanian officials for several hours but was finally released. I then went to Bucharest and sent a cablegram to an uncle in America. In it, I told him the situation and asked him to send me money.

When the money arrived, I went back to a spot near the border. There I used most of the money to bribe the Rumanian and Russian border guards and within a few days my mother and father and sisters were brought across the river and there was a happy reunion. I had also used some of the money to buy new clothes for all of them and to hire a fine carriage so that we might start the first day in something like our old style of living.

We went to Kishinev, only a few miles from the border. We found a place to live, and then there was the question of how we could support ourselves. We finally decided on publishing a Russian-language newspaper, but there was still another obstacle to overcome. A permit was necessary—not easy to get, since there were already several Russian-language papers in the area. The permits were granted by a Rumanian general who was in charge. I learned that he had a mistress who was vain about her appearance. I had been interested in art from an early age so I went and offered to do a portrait of her for nothing. She was pleased with the results and we received our permit.

By this time we had only six dollars left from the money my uncle had sent. It went to put out the first issue of our paper. My father was the business manager and the first issue was almost entirely written by myself. It was a modest success from the beginning and during the next two years we built the circulation up to between twelve and fifteen thousand copies. In addition to working on our newspaper, I wrote stories for other papers and attended art school.

In a way, we were happy. We were all together and making a living. But then, one day, a friend pointed out that we were still political refugees from Soviet Russia and that we were so near the Russian border we could never consider ourselves safe. He thought we should try to go to America where we'd surely be out of danger.

It was a good suggestion, but how were we—six people—going to get there? We had talked to other Russians in Rumania who wanted to go to America. We had heard all the stories about the long line of people outside the American embassy hoping for visas. Everybody agreed that it was impossible to get even one visa. Those were the facts, but I was young—barely nineteen by this time—and felt that nothing was impossible. I decided to go and get the visas.

I had no plan and very little money but there was one thing that helped. Newspaper editors were given free transportation in Rumania. I took what little money we could spare and boarded the train for Bucharest.

I knew only a few people in the city. I went first to visit one of these. There were several other Russians present and I was invited to go with them to church services next day. It was a special service on the anniversary of the assassination of the Czar. I met them the next morning at the church. Throughout the services I was aware of a man a couple of rows ahead of me. The back of his head seemed familiar. When the service was over, he turned around and then I recognized him as a Russian who had been in Kishinev a few months earlier. He was broke and I'd given him enough money to go to Vienna. Now he was in Bucharest and looking prosperous.

He came over as soon as he saw me and told me that he had stopped in Bucharest instead of going on to Vienna and confirmed the fact that he was doing well. He offered to give me the money he'd borrowed. I refused it but told him that perhaps he could help me get to America. He thought about it a minute and told me to meet him the next day.

When I met him he took me to a café and to a table occupied by a single man. My friend introduced him as Prince Putyatin—obviously a Russian. The count asked my friend what I wanted. At the end of the questioning, he called for paper and pen and wrote a letter which he handed to the other man. He went back to his drink— vodka and pepper—and ignored us as we left.

Then I learned who he was. Prince Putyatin was the uncle of Queen Marie of Rumania and he had given me a letter to his niece.

The next morning I went to the palace with my letter. It was taken by one of the ladies-in-waiting. A few minutes later I had an audience with the Queen. She wanted to know all about me and why I wanted to go to America. When I'd answered her questions, she gave me a letter to the American Ambassador.

A long line of people stretched down the street in front of the embassy, but my letter got me into the office at once. The Ambassador read the letter and said that I could have a visa. It was then that I finally explained that I wanted six visas, not one. He referred to the letter and pointed out that it said nothing about six persons. I offered to go back and get another letter. He sighed heavily and told me not to bother; if I would come back the next morning with my father he'd see what could be done.

I rushed out and sent a telegram to Kishinev. Next morning my father was in Bucharest and a few hours later we had the six visas. All that was left was to arrange passage. I had some ideas about that, too. There were several Russian-language newspapers in Rumania. I managed to get myself listed as a correspondent for each one of them in return for the promise of sending them stories about the trip to America. I then went to the shipping lines and pointed out the advantages of a series of stories written from a ship on the way across the Atlantic. Before long I had free passage for the six of us. We sold our newspaper and got ready for the trip.

It was 1923 when we landed in America. We had little money but lots of hope.

The first thing I did was to get a job writing, on literature, art and the theatre, for *Novoye Russkoye Slovo*, a

Russian-language newspaper in New York City, and I still write for them occasionally. Because it was hardly a full-time job, I looked for something else and was soon employed doing designs for glassware. It was piece work and I quickly developed a system which enabled me to do three times the average amount of work. I even hired a boy to help me. And eventually my system was adopted for everyone in the organization.

I had been in America almost two years when I was approached by a man who intended to produce *Peter the Great*, by Merezhkovsky, in Madison Square Garden, with Paul Muni and Maurice Schwartz. He had read my articles on the theatre and wanted my advice on whom to hire to design the scenery and costumes. I suggested myself.

I did some preliminary sketches and was then taken to meet Schwartz, who was to make the final decision. He liked the sketches and I was hired. That was the beginning of a long career in the theatre.

During the next fifteen years I designed sets and costumes for more than a dozen well-known plays in New York (including one starring Elissa Landi, who became the godmother of my daughter Elissa), directed a number of movie shorts and documentaries, and served as art director of several movies. In addition, I painted two murals for Ben Marden's Riviera in New Jersey; and for the World's Fair in New York in 1939 I made two murals for the Heinz Building, the backgrounds for the Puerto Rico Pavilion, decorations for the Turkish Pavilion, vegetation dioramas for the General Motors Building, the mural for the Consolidated Edison Building, three dioramas for the Tilo Roofing Exhibit and the decorations for Maurice Gest's *Little Miracle Town.*

In the meantime, I was also the curator for the Roerich Museum in New York and lectured on art appreciation, stagecraft, motion pictures, surrealism and industrial design in the Metropolitan Museum of Art, Brooklyn Art Museum, Museum of Modern Art, National Academy of Design, Rockefeller Center. My scenic designs and paintings have appeared in *Theatre Arts Monthly; The American Theatre,* by John Anderson; *A History of the Theatre,* by Freedley and Reeves; and in a book entitled *Van Rosen—1926,* by David Burliuk. Paintings of mine have been acquired for the permanent collections of the University of Minnesota and Queens College.

In 1943 I inadvertently started a new career. A friend of mine asked me to do a folder for his arc-welding machine company. I did it as a favor. Then a friend of his wanted a similar folder. I did that one, too. As a result of those two folders a printer wanted me to come to work for him as an artist. I took the job. Among other things, this printer made paper boxes for the packaging of various objects. This was the era when the War Production Board cut down on the use of paper. One of the companies seriously affected was Elizabeth Arden's. She was forced to use a thinner box for her powder—but one strong enough to serve its purpose. My employer was trying to solve the problem but had no luck and I finally asked if I could try it. I was given one day to try to do what the others had failed to do in weeks of work.

I worked all day without success. But I stayed on that night, alone in the plant. Finally, at about four in the morning, I thought I had a box that would serve. I made a model of it and then stretched out on the couch in my employer's office.

I was awakened a few hours later by the excited printer. He had seen the model, had shown it to Elizabeth Arden and it had been approved. I was to fly to Washington immediately to obtain a patent.

From then on I was in the business of designing boxes. Today I hold the patents on many of the boxes you buy —from cosmetics and nail polish to soft drinks. I worked for most of the leading American corporations, finally as head of my own consulting and engineering company.

I also found time, when war came, to enter the New York Guard. I enlisted as a private but my experience in the Russian-Polish war was of value and in fifty-one weeks I was commissioned a second lieutenant. I received two more promotions, to the rank of captain, before the war was over. I still hold that rank in the reserve.

Being in the business of packaging, I became interested in the whole problem of communication with the consumer. As a result of this interest, I developed a machine known as the Van Rosen Videometric Comparator. It is an entirely new and unique electronic device for comparing and measuring legibility and visual impact of any message, whether on a package or in a visual advertisement of any kind. It eliminates guesswork and argument and is accurate within the range of 50 milliseconds to 10 seconds.

Once it was completed, I formed a corporation to manufacture and lease or sell the machine. The company was barely started when I had my stroke. When I came out of the hospital, it was obvious that I couldn't immediately operate the business by myself. I entered into a contract with two persons who were to run the company, with my wife and me the major stockholders. I'm afraid it hasn't worked out. As soon as I regain control of the business, I shall have to start all over again.

I tell all this so that you may have an impression of the man who in June, 1959, lay in a hospital bed, not knowing if he would live—and, if he lived, not knowing whether he would ever walk or talk again.

That man was, and *is*, Robert E. Van Rosen.

PART I

"If it's impossible, I'll do it."

ROBERT E. VAN ROSEN

1. "He'll Never Walk Again"

What is a stroke? Most of us use the word often without being quite sure whether a stroke means a heart attack, a blood clot, a hemorrhage, or some other mysterious thing. Doctors are apt to call it a cerebral vascular accident, or a cerebral thrombosis, or one of several other medical terms, but you'll not often see these terms used in this book.

Although there are certain head injuries which can produce a similar condition, a stroke is usually caused by one of three things. A blood clot may form in the brain, or in one of the main arteries to the brain, so that a section of it is deprived of much-needed blood. A blood vessel in the brain may rupture, again depriving the brain of its requirements. A tumor may form in the brain and its growth will also bring on a stroke. In any one of the three, what happens is that a part of the brain is damaged and, depending on which part it is, it will affect one entire side of your body, your ability to speak or to remember words and numbers, or even the ability to understand what someone is saying. However it affects the person, and there are many variations, it will to some degree or other affect him permanently—if he survives the stroke.

When it comes to the question of what causes strokes you run into a Tower of Babel. Doctors are split into various schools of thought about causes (and I will say more about this later), but the truth is that there has been so little sound research that little is known. Yet strokes kill more people every year than any other illness except heart disease and cancer. Between 500,000 and 800,000 people have strokes in America every year. There are about 2,000,000 people now living in this country who have had strokes and survived. A great many of these are in hospitals or nursing homes, living a vegetable life—existing rather than living. Many times it is because of ignorance on the part of their families and their doctors. A few have managed to recover enough to function—to take care of themselves and in some cases to take care of their families. I am one of these.

In almost "all the ills that man is heir to" there are nearly always signals which could be important if enough were known about these ills. In the case of stroke, while we may not know the basic cause, important warnings are overweight, high blood pressure, or hypertension.* Sometimes, however, we don't discover these symp-

---

* According to medical dictionaries, high blood pressure and hypertension mean the same thing. In practice, however, even in recent books written by physicians, hypertension is commonly used to describe a condition caused by chronic anxiety and it will be so used throughout this book.

toms until too late. In my own case, I suppose I could say that I had an early and dramatic warning. It was my first brush with death—but not the last.

It was in 1953. One of my legs suddenly became painful. I went to my doctor, who diagnosed it as a blood clot. He gave me 1,000,000 units of penicillin and it got much better—so much so that in June I went on my vacation. In the meantime, however, I had resigned from the company for whom I did packaging designs and had started my own company as a designing engineer consultant. It was a big step and the vacation failed to relax me. Then my mother died.

I returned to New York to take care of all the details, which entailed considerable walking. My leg began to hurt again and continued to do so through July and most of August, but I didn't think it was too serious.

Then, on August 20th, I began to cough blood. My regular physician, Dr. Carp, was out of town so I went to another doctor. He paid little or no attention to the pain in my leg and diagnosed my case as probable pneumonia. The condition persisted and the following day I was taken to a hospital in an ambulance. There, after various x rays and other tests, he concluded I merely had atypical pneumonia. He gave me small doses of antibiotics and other medication and I stayed in the hospital until the first of September. Then I was sent home.

I still had pains in my lungs and leg, pains so bad that I couldn't sleep in a bed. I used the chaise longue. This continued for about a week and a half. Then on September 11th I went to the refrigerator. I bent over to reach a lower shelf and suddenly I couldn't breathe. For a moment I felt complete panic. It seemed impossible to get air into my lungs and I knew that unless I could breathe very quickly I would die.

I have always had a favorite motto that guided my life: "If it's impossible, I'll do it." This came to my aid. I determined that I was going to get a breath no matter what the cost. I gathered all my strength and made the effort. The result felt as if something had broken inside me, but air did rush into my lungs. It was a wonderful feeling—like being reborn.

As soon as I called my doctor I was returned to the hospital. More tests were made. My doctor was still sure that I had pneumonia. But this time I had a bit of luck. On the third day I was moved into a semiprivate room with a doctor who was dying of cancer. He had been a lung specialist. He listened to the story of my symptoms and said the diagnosis was sheer nonsense. He thought that I had a thrombophlebitis with pulmonary embolism. As a result, my sister Beatrice insisted that my doctor consult with the head of the hospital.

This diagnosis was confirmed. A surgeon was called. At first he was going to operate on my legs but decided there was not enough time. There was also a blood clot in the inferior *vena cava*, a vein which runs along the spine. He planned on doing the operation the following day but Beatrice insisted that if there were any danger of my dying in the interval the operation should be done immediately. So I was wheeled into the operating room almost as soon as the decision was made.

The operation consisted of opening my stomach, re-

34

moving all of my intestines so that they could reach the spine from the front. Then the vein was tied so that there could be no more spreading of the clot. It was a long operation and I had to be given three pints of blood in the process.

This was on September 16th, five days after I had entered the hospital for the second time. The operation was a complete success but I can't honestly say that I felt good. My legs were still badly swollen and very painful. I had to have surgical bandages on them which had to be changed daily. I also had pain from the operation so I was given narcotics every few hours. This was, however, not a stroke, even though it was caused by a blood clot as some strokes are. There was no paralysis, and I was fully conscious.

I think it was the first or second day after the operation that I heard two doctors discussing me in the hallway outside my room.

"What's the difference if he can never walk again?" one of them said. "We saved his life, didn't we?"

2. It Strikes

That was a shock. It had never occurred to me that once the operation was a success everything wouldn't be exactly as it had been before. For a few minutes I confess I was depressed. Then I rejected what the doctor had said. "The hell I won't walk!" I told myself, and that thought was uppermost in my mind for the next few months.

That was September 17th. On October 29th I left the hospital and went home but still had to stay in bed with my legs elevated most of the time. However, I did manage to do some limited office work at home.

Throughout, I held to my determination to walk. Whenever I could I would try a few steps in the apartment. Finally, early in March, 1954, four months after leaving the hospital, I ventured out of the apartment for the first time. I went to buy a newspaper. To do so, I had to cross the street and then walk about a block. Halfway there I had to sit down on the steps of a house and rest.

But I reached the newsstand and bought my paper. On the way back, I stopped and rested on the same steps.

I have done many things in my life but I think that one of my most triumphant moments was when I got back to the apartment with my newspaper. I remember thinking that I wished my walk could have been witnessed by the doctor who had said I would never walk again.

From then on, the progress was slow but steady. A month later I had my first full day out alone, walking most of the time. I went to the spring auto show. It was a wonderful feeling.

It was necessary for me to wear elastic, full-length stockings on both legs—still wear knee-length ones—and when I began to walk I had difficulty keeping them up. Someone suggested that I get a woman's garter belt or girdle but I didn't like the idea. Finally I got a man's girdle and sewed snaps onto it and thus managed to keep the stockings from slipping down.

On one of my visits to my surgeon, he suggested I had better take medication for high blood pressure. I have been taking a combination of Singoserp and Esidrix since then and this has generally kept my blood pressure within safe limits.

By September, 1954, I was able to set up new offices on 57th Street. I went to the office regularly although I did have to keep my legs elevated for several hours each day. I continued to work throughout that winter, and the following spring moved my offices to 56th Street. By the summer of 1955, almost two years after I had gone to the hospital, I was completely recovered. I did have to wear the elastic stockings and take medication for my blood pressure but I could walk normally and carry a full schedule of work just as well as I had before the operation. I believe that at that time only one other man had completely recovered from the operation in which the *vena cava* is tied, out of eight or nine people who had it. His name is Ben Hogan.

All this time I was still active in my business as a package designer. I had worked for nearly all the large corporations in America and had received many awards, among them the 1952 Grand Award for the Coca-Cola Picnic Carrier, but it was a special triumph three years after my operation to receive the 1956 Merit Award for a talking carton I designed for the United States Rubber Company. So much, I thought, for the doctor who had said I'd never walk again.

The following year I decided to introduce a change in my business—the subscription service described earlier. I worked out a formal presentation and sent it out. The results were deeply disappointing. One company subscribed for a year and another took the service for a six-month period. The other companies were still interested but would not commit themselves. It brought in barely enough money to keep the office going but I decided to continue in hope that the others would soon come in.

Something else interested me in the meantime. I had always done my best work when there was a specific challenge. I had originated and patented many startling new ideas in packaging but I had never been able to do this in a vacuum. If someone came to me with a problem which could not be solved, I would sit down and work until I had the answer. There was one such over-all problem in the field and I was turning my attention to it.

This problem is one of legibility. It applies not only to the printed matter on boxes and packages but to book jackets, window displays, television commercials, and many other forms of commercial communication. The problem is to make sure that a particular combination of picture, words, and color attract the consumer's attention and then clearly deliver the message to him. This problem, simple as it may seem, has probably caused more arguments in advertising agencies and business offices than anything else. It had always been a personal and emotional decision with no means of scientifically measuring a visual message—until I discovered the way.

The year was 1958. I finally succeeded in inventing an electronic device, which I called the Van Rosen Videometric Comparator, that accurately evaluated any visual message. It can help select the most effective layout, color scheme, typography, headline copy, logo, box design, label design, and the like. It can measure, in split seconds, how long it takes a message to reach the person intended. I immediately formed the R. E. Van Rosen Corporation to sell or lease this machine. A number of America's largest corporations began to make use of it, among them American Can Company, Armstrong Cork Company, Inc., Container Corporation of America, and Sunshine Biscuits, Inc.

In the meantime, however, I had two businesses going, both with great potentialities, but they were barely holding their own. This meant that I had to do a lot of work myself that I would have usually hired someone else to do and that there were many annoyances and frustrations. I have never been known for great patience or sweetness of temper, so that was not an easy period. I remember once delivering a number of heavy boxes by taxi and the driver refused to help me. In anger, I carried the boxes myself. A few hours later I had a very bad attack of dizziness. I went to see my doctor, who diagnosed it as Ménière's syndrome, a disturbance of the inner ear. He thought it might have been brought on by my anger at the cab driver. It did go away in a few hours and never reappeared. More recently, however, another doctor has told me that I may have had a "small" stroke at the time, resulting in acute labyrinthitis, something very similar to Ménière's syndrome.

Things went on pretty much the same for the next seven months. I felt well physically, but the business was not doing well and this was a constant irritant. Several times I thought of giving up the office but I stubbornly held on in the hope that it would pick up. In addition to the frustration, it meant long hours of hard work on my part.

Early in the spring of 1959 I began to experience a slight numbness in my right arm. It would last for only a few moments and then go away. There were long intervals between these attacks, but after I'd had several of them I was worried enough to go to a doctor. (The two doctors who had treated me for the thrombophlebitis were dead and so I found a new doctor.) He gave me a complete physical examination, then sent me to a neurologist for another examination, which included an electroencephalogram, or a recording of the brain waves to see if there were any evidence of a brain tumor. The conclusions, when they came in from both doctors, were that I was in good health.

That was the picture June 13, 1959, as I have mentioned earlier. I was in "good health," according to the doctors. I had a lovely, wonderful young wife. It was a glorious spring day. It was true that my business was not doing well, but a day in the country could help me to forget that.

The beginning was not, however, auspicious for a quick-tempered man. We missed the train and had to wait for another one. I cannot now remember my exact feelings at the time but I'm sure I must have glowered at everything and everybody on the ride to Connecticut. But once there and out on our friends' boat, I relaxed and began to enjoy myself. My arm was still bothering me but I didn't worry about it even when I was unable to use it to get the lobster meat out of the shell. Nor was I unduly worried at the evening meal when my wife had to help me with cutting the meat.

I think now, looking back, that I first began to worry slightly on our way home when I found that I could not say some words as distinctly as usual. I'd had several drinks but certainly not enough to affect my speech.

It was about midnight when we arrived home. By that time I was aware that something was wrong. I discussed it with my wife, who thought that I should call my doctor. Still, one is hesitant to call a doctor at such a late hour. I phoned my sister Beatrice and talked to her about it. She also insisted that I get in touch with my doctor. So finally I called him.

As I have already related he at first wanted to know if it couldn't wait until the next day. When I told him that I wasn't sure that I would be able to talk to him the following day he immediately agreed to come. He asked me for the address and for the first time in my life I was unable to say something that I knew as well as I knew anything. I had to hand the phone over to my wife.

My doctor arrived within a few minutes and examined me. He told me that he thought I'd had a stroke and that I should go to the hospital at once. He phoned for an ambulance.

3. This Is a Stroke

My first reaction, when I was admitted to the hospital shortly after midnight, was that this stroke couldn't really be very serious. It was true that I couldn't properly use my right arm, that my entire right side felt peculiar, that my speech was slurred, but otherwise I felt fine. My mind was perfectly clear and I felt sure that everything else would soon be corrected.

The reality of the situation was that my doctor's prognosis was "guarded" that night and for the following ten days—which meant he wasn't sure whether I'd live or not. In fact, he ordered nurses around the clock for me the moment I entered the hospital. My sister Ahda took the job of trying to get the first nurse and since by then it was about two-thirty in the morning on a Sunday this was by no means easy. She accomplished it, however, and it wasn't too long before I went to sleep. That was the beginning of about six weeks in the hospital.

The next morning they began to make all sorts of tests

to verify the diagnosis of a stroke and to try to make sure what kind of stroke it was. Except for the same symptoms I'd had the night before, I still felt fine and wasn't in the least bit worried. I had a telephone in my room, and between tests I kept in touch with my office and tried to continue running the business. My wife and sisters were opposed to this but any attempt to stop me only irritated me. I was positive that there was nothing seriously wrong with me and that I had to keep things going for the few days I'd be away from the office.

The tests continued for the next three days, without a final decision, and then on the fourth day, June 17th, my condition suddenly became much worse. There is some question as to exactly why. My doctor believes that I had only the original stroke and that it was only then that the full force hit me. The hospital records state that I suffered a second stroke on June 17th. Whatever the reason, the right side of my face and body became completely paralyzed, I couldn't speak more than two words, and my temperature began to rise.

My sister Beatrice suggested a new medicine that had not been used in stroke cases. My doctor tried it. But even that did not seem to help and my temperature went up to 105 degrees. The new medicine was stopped. Then, as strangely as it started to rise, my temperature began to drop.

The next several days were almost a blank to me. I couldn't talk or even think. I don't believe I understood anything that was said to me. I knew that I was alive—and dimly I was aware of a determination to continue living—but otherwise there was nothing. I knew that I existed and at the moment all of my energies were directed toward continuing that existence. Nothing else was important.

In the meantime, of course, everyone else was deeply concerned. My wife, my sisters, my daughter, and my doctor were all aware how thin was the thread that held me to life and I'm sure that in many respects it was worse for them than for me. I knew that I was alive and that I was determined to stay alive; at the moment I did not need to know more.

This lasted about a week. Then I began to grow more aware of what was going on. I could understand more of what was being said around me, although I doubt if I could say more than four or five words, not always correctly. For the first time I knew that whatever had happened to me was bigger and more serious than I had thought. It would be another month before I would fully comprehend this, and even longer before I accepted all that it meant; but at least it was a beginning.

I also began to be aware, and to appreciate, how much my family was standing by. My sisters Beatrice, Ahda, and Rhyissa came to the hospital whenever they were free. My daughter Elissa spent many hours reading to me. My wife came every morning before going to work and then hurried back to the hospital the minute her work was done. I know that many a day she stayed until the visiting hours were over, then stopped off in some drugstore for a hasty hamburger and went home to fall into bed exhausted. I was very fortunate to be surrounded by five such women, and even more fortunate that one of them was my wife. I have never forgotten this, although a stroke makes one forget many things.

Beatrice made sure that I had a television set in my room as soon as I was able to pay attention to anything. This was a big help to me. I could understand everything that was said to me, although I couldn't answer, which made most conversations very frustrating for me. I could watch television and understand what was happening but there was no demand for me to answer, so it represented a form of relaxed communication with the rest of the world. I spent many hours with it, then and later, which I believe made my recovery much easier.

Once I became even slightly more aware of what was going on, many things about my own personality became important—as it does with everyone who suffers a stroke. I had always been a very active man, as I have already indicated, directing my own destiny with assurance and always in command of every situation. Now, suddenly, I was robbed of this ability. The result was a frustration which often filled me with anger even in those first days when I was not feeling too much. On the other hand, I had always believed that if something were impossible I would do it, so that I had a tremendous drive to overcome everything that had happened to me. From the minute I could think at all, I was determined that I would not be defeated.

In the meantime, all the possible tests had been made save one. That was angiography—in which a special dye is injected into the arteries so that they can be X-rayed to locate a blood clot—but it was decided that my condition was not good enough to go through that particular test. But the diagnosis was that I had a cerebral vascular occlusion(the same as cerebral vascular accident) and that the blood clot was probably located in the left cerebral artery. In other words, it was official that I had a stroke.

Something else happened at this time which gave me a big psychological lift. My wife told the doctor that it had been our custom to have Martinis before dinner every Friday and Monday night and asked him if I could have a drink while I was in the hospital. He said I could. So each Friday and Monday she brought in all the ingredients and the glasses and we had our Martinis together. It was another link to my usual life and made it easier for me to fight back.

At the end of my second week in the hospital, July 1, 1959, it was decided that I was ready for physical therapy. The Department of Physical Medicine and Rehabilitation at the New York Polyclinic Hospital, where I was, was temporarily closed for vacation so Dr. Zofia Laszewski, Director of Physical Medicine, obtained the services of a physical therapist named Nathan Melniker. I owe much of my comeback to these two people.

Mr. Melniker started treating me on July 3rd. His first report states that I "demonstrated right facial weakness, marked weakness of the right upper extremity [my arm], especially of the muscles of the wrist, hand and fingers. . . . There was also present a painful shoulder syndrome which appeared most marked upon extension of the wrist.

The right lower extremity [my leg] demonstrated some weakness. However no muscle group appeared to test weaker than Fair plus. Resistance exercises were commenced on July 3rd. However, the patient's condition worsened over the weekend and on the night of July 6th there was a great increase in pain and a marked flaccidity of the musculature of the entire right arm. . . . Treatment at this stage consisted of heat and massage to the shoulder area. Range of motion exercise to all the joints of the right upper extremity' with pain as the limiting factor. . . ."

There is one thing missing from the report which I think was important in my case. From the beginning, Mr. Melniker insisted that I try to walk without aids of any sort. There are many stroke cases where the patient has to use parallel bars, a walking belt, or at least a cane; but he felt that in my case that would be a mistake. It was, I think, a wise decision. It represented a challenge to me, and that was something which always stimulated me.

The hospital reports for this period mention that on July 6th I had more "sensory attacks," also in Mr. Melniker's report; that on July 13th I was "doing well" but couldn't "protrude tongue"; on July 22nd it included the fact that I had a "stiff tongue . . . some improvement in sensory reactions. . . . Toilet activities independent." The latter merely meant that I was able to walk to the bathroom. It also mentioned that I was getting facial and tongue exercises.

In the meantime, I was doing certain things on my

own. One of the first things was to refuse to be shaved by the barber who made the rounds in the hospital every day. My wife brought my electric razor and I began to use it with my left hand. I began to remember a few more words but also to develop a sign language that conveyed what I wanted when I couldn't find a word. I think that much of this was accomplished because I did not believe that I was going to be crippled in any way. What had happened to me was merely an illness, like any other, and I would recover from it as I had from the operation six years before.

There were reasons, or so it seemed at the time, which contributed to this thinking. I was making progress. Much of the feeling had returned to my right leg and I was able to walk without outside assistance. Some words were coming back to me and by the end of July I was able to say about a hundred words. If I had been able to make that much progress in the six weeks I'd been in the hospital, I thought at the time, certainly it would not be long before I would be as well as I had been before the stroke.

As though to confirm my optimism, I was sent home on July 31, 1959.

4. The Road Back

Although I was unaware of it at the time, considerable preparation had been made for my return. My wife, Marcia, had spent many hours with the doctors and the physical therapist trying to anticipate all the problems that might arise. We lived then, as we do now, in a penthouse with a very large terrace. That terrace has always been my pride and joy and Marcia knew that it would be important for me to be able to reach it whenever I wanted to. There is an elevation of a few inches from the living room to the terrace. Marcia measured it carefully and Mr. Melniker saw to it, while I was still in the hospital, that I learned to get my right leg over that height.

Marcia also learned other things that might give me difficulties and made other preparations for my return home. She removed all the buttons from my pajama trousers and sewed in elastic cord so that I could put them on and remove them myself. She rearranged the furniture so that there would be a minimum of obstacles in my path as I walked around the house. Since she knew how much pleasure television had given me in the hospital, she bought a set with remote control and placed a comfortable chair in front of it. The chair was a reclining one, since it would be important for me to keep my legs elevated for some time each day.

So I arrived home to an apartment which had been made as adaptable to my needs as it could be. Besides, Marcia had decided that we should do something positive about improving my speech. Mr. Melniker suggested two kinds of "flash" cards, one dealing with numbers for children from kindergarten through grade 1 and the other dealing with words for children in grades 1 through 3. In both cases, the numbers and words are coupled with pictures, making it easier to learn, or, in my case, to relearn.

Marcia was working full time and a good thing, for the hospital and medical expenses had pretty well drained our resources despite the insurance. She would get up early every morning, make and serve breakfast, then sit down to teach me speaking and writing before going off to work. She would also arrange things so that I could get my own lunch. She would put in a full day at the office, come home and make dinner and wash the dishes, then sit down to work with me again on speech and writing therapy. Little wonder that she was exhausted every night.

When she'd leave in the morning I would usually spend extra time practicing my writing. My period of concentration was limited, as it is with everyone who has had a stroke, and I could never work at it very long. The same was true of reading. I had always done a lot of reading but now I found that I could read only a few minutes at a time. And when I picked up a book I'd begun, I found that I couldn't remember what I'd already covered. It was very frustrating and I'd often turn back to television, which gave me many hours of entertainment.

I did not, however, spend my whole day glued to the television set. As I've said before, I had not yet accepted the full reality of what had happened to me. I was positive that it was only a matter of time, and hard work on my part, before I would be able to do everything as well as before. So I'd spend as much time as I could on the terrace or walking around the apartment. Then at about three in the afternoon my physical therapist would arrive and I'd work with him. I'd watch television again after he left, until Marcia came home. We might have a cocktail or two, then dinner, and afterward more work on my speech and writing.

I had been home about two weeks when I suddenly decided I wanted to get out of the apartment. Marcia and I went to a movie three blocks from our apartment, walking both ways. We got home shortly before the therapist arrived. He was horrified when I told him what I had done. However, I was too tired to go through the therapy session and had to lie down to rest.

In September, about six weeks after I had left the hospital, we decided that perhaps I should have a professional speech therapist. We hired one to come to the house to work with me, but after only a few sessions I decided she wasn't helping me and I went back to working with Marcia.

We had always entertained a lot and we tried to continue that habit. Marcia and my sisters also thought it would be good for me. In a way it was good to have my family and my old friends in for the evening, but in another way it was frustrating. As I've indicated, I had always been a very active and social person. In the old days such parties more or less centered about me. I always had a fund of stories and was urged to tell them. Now, suddenly, I could no longer do this. I would try to tell a story but the right words wouldn't come. Everyone was sympathetic, which made it worse, for I could feel them straining and hoping I would remember the words. That, in turn, would make me more tense and nothing would come out. Still, I did enjoy seeing people and I'm sure it did help to some degree. Quite a few of my old friends said they were delighted to have a chance to get a word in at last.

I'd been out of the hospital about two months when I got the worst shock of my life.

I was home alone. I can't recall the exact circumstances but I suspect I must have tried to do something with my right arm and failed. Then it hit me—the realization I'd been trying to deny since I'd had my stroke. I was going to be crippled for the rest of my life.

They say that your past life flashes before you when you're drowning. I don't know about that, but it certainly happened to me with this realization. I looked back over my life from the time I had been growing up in Russia and compared it with what I was facing.

A dozen questions flashed through my mind. On one wall of our living room there is a case filled with medals I had won in pistol and rifle matches. How would I be able to shoot again with my right arm paralyzed? I looked at my paintings on the walls and at my scrapbook of stage settings and package designs. How could I work at my chosen profession without the use of that same right arm? Or, for that matter, how could I even make a living at anything? I thought of the many other things I had enjoyed—going out, dancing, swimming, my life in the New York State Guard. I could see no place in my future for any of these things.

Then there was my wife. I knew how much she had done for me since the stroke; but then perhaps she too had been telling herself that I would soon be as well as ever. How would she feel when she realized . . . ? After all, she was many years younger than I. How could she, or any other woman, face a future of being tied down to a crippled man?

At the time, I could find no answers to these questions. I sat down and cried.

This depressed mood lasted, I think, for about three days. I never mentioned it to Marcia or anyone else, but when I was alone I would be overcome with self-pity and despair. I cried many times, often at night when I was in bed.

I imagine that every stroke victim goes through this depression and I've been told that many of them remain

in it. But after a few days of this my old personality began to emerge again.

"I'll be damned," I told myself, "if I'm going to be a
cripple."

I didn't know exactly what I meant or what I planned
to do about it, but I was determined that I wasn't going
to let it get me down. I would find some way to overcome the handicap and once more do things I enjoyed.

One of the things necessary was to improve my speech.
Marcia and I had made some progress but not enough.
If anything, I knew I must learn to express myself much
better. I went to Dr. Laszewski for evaluation and advice. Although the hospital has a very fine speech therapy
department, the doctor suggested that I go to Hunter
College since it is within walking distance of my apartment. I went there in November and was tested by
Dr. Doris T. Leberfeld.

The first report on that test included the following:
"Difficulty in articulation.
Difficulty in naming colors.
Difficulty in abstract thoughts.
Difficulty in reading and with numbers.
Couldn't match letters (2 L's, for example).
Counted well up to 10.
Difficulty in graphic expression.
Could copy numbers but not always name them.
Couldn't spell orally.
Difficulty in telling time."

It concluded by saying that my visual comprehen-
sions were good but slow, that I used a phonetic ap-

proach (that is, sounds rather than letters) and that I had nominal, numerical and graphic speech difficulties. It recommended that I start therapy as soon as possible.

On December 3rd, I began my speech therapy with Mrs. Joyce Buck at Hunter College.

She soon had me working equally hard on speech and writing and we were making progress. I'm afraid, however, that it was often too slow to still my impatience. I decided to devote most of my work to speech, at the expense of the writing. If I could learn to speak well enough, I reasoned, I could always tell someone what to write for me but I could hardly get anyone to speak for me. I have never regretted that decision.

I also continued with the physical therapy although the sessions were less frequent and I did more on my own. I worked out methods for getting dressed easily with one hand, trying to make myself as self-sufficient as possible. In those early days I wore shoes without laces, but later I was to learn to tie a shoelace with one hand. At first I used bow ties that clipped on but I also soon learned to knot a regular tie with one hand. It was a slow progress, and many times I became angry with frustration, but I was going forward.

During this period I had two interesting experiences. I was so determined not to be a cripple that I was willing to do anything. When somebody suggested that perhaps hypnosis might help, I lost no time in getting in touch with a psychiatrist who sometimes used hypnotism. I made my first appointment.

I was optimistic after our first talk, for the doctor had

done considerable psychiatric research with stroke patients. He had never tried hypnotism in such cases and was doubtful of any good result but he was willing to try. That was all I needed—or so I thought.

It turned out that something more was needed—from me. While I was anxious to try hypnosis, I apparently had an unconscious resistance to giving up even that much control of myself. Instead of entering into a hypnotic state, I went to sleep every time we tried to work. No amount of effort on my part, or on the doctor's, could change this and we finally had to give up. I still think, however, that if I'd been able to cooperate it might have helped. I don't think it would have cured my paralysis but it might have been useful in regaining my speech.

Despite this failure, I was still ready to try anything. It was then that someone told me about H3. Some time before, Professor Anna Aslan, Director of the Institute of Geriatrics in Bucharest, had started using injections of novocain on her patients. She had claimed startling results in rejuvenation and in the cure of various ills. Pictures of the before-and-after variety had been published. She had been visited by many doctors and medical journalists, some of whom reported that they had seen these miracles. Others, by far the majority, were more skeptical.

Professor Aslan admitted that she didn't know what it was in novocain that produced the results but stoutly claimed that they were all valid. Because she didn't know what the unknown factor was she called it H3, believing it to be related to two members of the B-complex of vitamins known as H1 and H2.

I'm not quite certain what I expected H3 to do for me, but somewhere deep inside I nursed a small hope that it might bring life back to my right arm. After all, it had rejuvenated the aged. . . . Even though one may accept a paralyzed arm, it is probably a long time before the secret hope for a miracle is lost.

We found a doctor in New York who gave the injections regularly for twelve weeks, then there would be a period in which they would be stopped, after which I would return for another twelve weeks. I was warned not to expect quick results.

I finished the twelve weeks and went home to wait for something to happen. It seemed like a long wait but at last something did happen—at least, it seemed to be related to the injections. It wasn't, however, what I'd been looking and hoping for.

Like many men today, I'd been losing my hair for some time. Suddenly it started growing again. I can't claim that I grew a full head of luxuriant hair, but quite a bit of new hair did come in before it stopped.

If it can grow hair, I thought, perhaps it can accomplish other wonders; so when it was time for another series of treatments I phoned the doctor. It was a shock to find out that he had died in the interval. Most of us, I'm sure, feel that doctors shouldn't die, and when it's a doctor with a miracle treatment the disappointment is magnified.

I was still interested in H3 and thought I'd find another man who would give me the injections. I spoke to my own doctor about it. He had been opposed when I first went for the treatment and was now even more so. He felt so strongly about it that I finally decided to follow his advice. He had saved my life and it would be foolish to ignore him for someone who had done nothing for me. Somewhat regretfully I abandoned the idea of H3. I still sometimes wonder what might have happened if I had decided otherwise, but I'm also aware that I might have gone on looking for miracles instead of accomplishing what I have by my own effort.

Once the decision was made, I went back to concentrating entirely on making my own salvation. I worked hard on the physical and speech therapy and knew I was making progress. My ability to concentrate was increasing, my speech was getting better, and my physical movements had improved. I was exercising my right arm daily and could move it considerably. Although there was no feeling in the arm at all, and very little grasp in the hand, I was learning that I could carry things by pressing the object against my body. A few things dropped but I kept doggedly at it.

I continued searching for ways to make things easier. My physical therapist secured a fork and spoon with special handles for people handicapped as I was, and I tried to learn to eat with my right hand. This, however, proved too difficult and I went back to learning to use my left.

During the cold weather Marcia and I often took walks. I soon discovered that the glove on my right hand would often drop off and, because there was no feeling in the hand, I wouldn't discover it for several blocks. Marcia sewed a snap fastener on that glove and I had no more trouble with it. There was a special triumph in each new discovery.

By January, 1960, I felt it was time for me to start proving how much progress I'd made. Besides, Marcia had been carrying the financial burden and I wanted to relieve her of that. I decided to go back to my office. I wouldn't be able to do any package designing yet, but I could start trying to sell the machine I had invented. Many advertising agencies and companies had expressed interest in it from the beginning. I was sure that it would sell. The only problem was that I wouldn't be able to go out and make all the necessary calls. My sister Rhyissa volunteered to help. We moved into the office that month.

There was a couch in the office so that I could rest during the day when no one was around. Rhyissa was out doing the preliminary sales job, but then interested people would come to the office to see the machine and get a closing sales talk from me. This brought up a new problem. I was still very sensitive about my paralyzed right arm, especially when it came to shaking hands. I could lift the arm all right but I was unable to grasp the other hand, and I felt that many persons didn't like shaking a limp hand. But if I tried to shake with my left hand it was unexpected and confused the other person. Since there was nothing visibly wrong with my right hand they would become curious. I solved the problem by wearing a sling on the arm during office hours.

I think that I've already indicated that mine was a close-knit family. If anything occurred to a member, my three sisters would be on hand almost immediately, doing whatever was necessary. They had demonstrated that when I went to the hospital with my stroke. Rhyissa demonstrated it again when she quit her job and came to help me sell my machine—especially so since I'm sure I gave her a rough time in the seven months she worked with me.

A stroke does not change one's personality. It does usually exaggerate many of his reactions. I had never been famous for patience. I had always expected the impossible from all, especially myself. This new venture was no exception.

The situation was difficult enough as it was. The Van Rosen Videometric Comparator is a complicated machine performing a complex job. It was also a new concept in the field of measuring communication between buyer and seller. I was probably the only person who fully understood it. While my speech had improved greatly, even I was aware that I couldn't give a long sales talk on a successful level, nor could I have physically stood the strain of such work day after day. Rhyissa was an attractive young woman, intelligent and personable, but all she knew about the machine was what I had been able to instill in her in a short period of time.

Also, there was the fact that while many companies were interested in the Comparator, many felt that it should be tested more before they invested in the machine. There was a caution in their response, as always when a new concept is being put into practice.

I, on the other hand, felt a great urgency to start the sales pouring in. I wanted to prove that I could run my business again. But that was only part of it. My illness and the medical expenses, despite the fact that they were partly covered by insurance, had pretty well exhausted our finances and there was little money to carry on the business.

All these things served to heighten a tension already present. When sales didn't immediately come in I began to go into rages. I'm sure that my anger was mostly at myself because I couldn't do the things I expected of myself, but Rhyissa bore the brunt of most of them. Despite this, she stayed on with me, working very hard, until I closed the office seven months after we had started. We had made a couple of sales, to General Foods Corporation and to Schenley Industries, Inc., but that was not enough. There was no point in going on.

It was a great disappointment to me. I had been so pleased with my progress during the months before returning to the office and had been sure that Rhyissa and I could make it work. What was probably true was that I had tried to take too big a step. If I had only waited until I was more ready it might have been a different story.

Still, at the time, I went home and faced the truth: if I wanted anything done with my invention I'd have to get somebody else to do it. I was still in therapy and still doing well, but another attempt to run the business myself was out of the question. I began to look around for interested and competent people.

Finally, in October, I thought I had found those I wanted. They were a man and woman who seemed greatly interested in the machine and made a satisfactory offer. They were to pay me immediately a certain sum and revive the business. Marcia and I would remain stockholders and on the board of directors. They would also pay me a certain sum every week. It seemed a good solution and we entered into the agreement.

A few weeks later, in November, it was agreed that I had made enough progress to discontinue both the physical and the speech therapy. I still worked on my own but it was felt I no longer needed the therapists. I think it restored some of my belief in myself.

The next four months were mostly devoted to my schedule, but toward the end of that period another irritant arose. Things were not going well with the new corporation setup. It seemed to me that the two people were not approaching it in the right way; they were certainly having little success. They had already fallen far behind on the regular payments.

Then, early in 1961, we planned to take one of our machines to Chicago for an exhibition. I was to go along with them. Again we clashed about what was to be done at the exhibition. We finally reached a compromise but not until I had gone through many days of constant irritation.

Then, just before I was supposed to go to Chicago, my right leg once more became paralyzed.

5. The Second Road Back

Again, there is some disagreement about what happened to me to cause paralysis of my right leg. Some medical authorities believe that I suffered another, but minor, stroke. Others believe that I merely had a setback. Whatever the reason, it was serious enough that I had to use a wheel chair. And I was sent back to the hospital for a week where I was kept on a high level of anticoagulant drugs, with vitamin K on hand in case of hemorrhage.

There is, I think, an interesting pattern in my experiences. Before I had the stroke I had gone through a long period of anxiety and frustration because of my business. I'd often been angry. Now, again, I'd been through a year of the same sort of tensions, and then when I thought I had the business solved my new associates had turned out to be other than I had expected. Each time I had reacted very much the same way, although this time it was less serious than before.

I am not trying to offer a new medical diagnosis, but

64

I do think there was a definite relationship between my illness and what was happening to me. Much has been written about what modern stresses do to health; many doctors have gone further in linking the two things together, but I've seen nothing on it in reference to strokes.

When I left the hospital after a week I was able to walk again, although not quite as well as previously. In other ways, I think, there was a general slackening in my progress and in my drive to overcome my disability. It is difficult now to describe what I was going through but there was no doubt that I was in a slump. This was more obvious to others than to me.

That spring Marcia wanted to go to Europe for her vacation. I didn't feel like taking such a long trip but I urged Marcia to go ahead while I took a short vacation in the country. She was reluctant to do so, but I convinced her that it was all right and she went.

A few days later I took off for the country. Although I missed Marcia I was able to get around fine alone and enjoyed myself at first. Then I began to feel worse and was conscious of pain in the scar of my old thrombophlebitis operation. When it persisted I called my doctor in New York. He refused to commit himself over the phone and suggested that I return to the city immediately. So my vacation was quickly over.

When I got back the doctor soon diagnosed the trouble. I had developed a blood clot in the scar left by the operation. I went through another intense anticoagulant treatment and the clot slowly dissolved.

Marcia came back from Europe in June. She'd had a wonderful time but felt contrite when she heard what had happened to my vacation. I assured her that it hadn't been dangerous and that she could have done nothing even if she had been here. Just the same I was secretly glad she was back.

At this time I had been in a general slump for eight months. I could still walk and speak almost as well but there had been no progress. I was beginning to be depressed by the situation. Then, suddenly, with the return of Marcia there was a dramatic improvement all around. My physical efforts were better, my speech rapidly improved again, and the same difference was noticeable in my mental abilities.

Not too long before, I couldn't concentrate more than fifteen minutes—and even that had been achieved by many months of hard work; but now it was soon up to forty-five minutes. Among other things it meant that I could once more read and retain enough of it to pick up wherever I left off. It was a good feeling. Once more I felt hopeful, and regained my determination to overcome as much of the handicap as was humanly possible. Or maybe even impossible.

That summer, in addition to my physical and speech exercises, I worked in my garden. As I have mentioned, we have a large terrace with our apartment, with many flowers and shrubs and two fruit trees. Every summer I grow our own tomatoes. I did all the work myself and found it invigorating. For the first time I began to think more about the future than just my struggle to walk and talk.

For one thing, I began to think about writing this book. As soon as I was able to read after my stroke I had searched for everything published about the subject. Quite a few such books are available but I discovered that almost none of them gave any real practical help to the person who had a stroke or to his family. It had taken me many months to find a book that told me how to tie my shoelaces with one hand. There were other things which I had learned by trial and error; still others I had tracked down over the past two and a half years, finding one bit of information here, another there.

I knew that strokes were the Number 3 killer in the United States, after cancer and heart disease, but that very little money had been spent on research; and there were many things about which even doctors admitted they didn't know. I knew that there were two million of us who had survived strokes and that our number was increasing by several hundred thousand each year. All had faced the same problems I had, some more seriously and some less, and their families faced the same problems as had involved Marcia, my three sisters, and my daughter.

In a way I had been lucky, living in New York City where it was easier to find out about therapy centers, and to reach them; where there was easy access to books that could tell me something about what had happened to me. But many stroke victims live in small towns scattered over the country, with no access to these things, and in many cases they are treated by doctors who know nothing about the availability of therapy, are completely ignorant about the self-help aids which can be procured, and often don't bother to find out about them. As a result, many such stroke victims never make much of a comeback and many are in institutions or must be cared for constantly by their families.

I'd been thinking about this for some time and I'd decided that as soon as I could I would tell the story of my stroke, and help others with the information it had taken me so long to gather.

I now felt the time had come when I could write the book. With the aid of my sister Beatrice, I worked up an outline. I had several copies made and mailed them out to the publishers. It was then November, 1961.

In the meantime, nothing was happening with my Comparator and I had trouble getting any answers from the two people who were running the corporation. It was a constant state of irritation but I was learning to cope with it somewhat better than before, and there were apparently no bad effects on my health. Improvement continued—slowly, but in a way that I could see.

Then, early in 1962, I heard from one of the publishers. I went in to see the editor and we quickly came to terms. It had been obvious to me all along that when it came time to do the book I would need help. As I mentioned in the preface, I had done some writing throughout most of my life but I could no longer use a typewriter, and writing itself was the one area in which

I had made the least progress. The editor suggested several persons and I made a decision. The contract for the publication of the book was signed in February and the work started immediately.

Early in the work on the book I decided that I would like to again take the various tests that had been given to me two and a half years earlier. I called Dr. Laszewski and made my request. She agreed that it might be interesting and immediately made all the arrangements.

The first person I saw was Mr. Melniker. He had made his first report on me when he started treating me while I was still in the hospital so he had seen me long before anyone else in the hospital. In that first report Mr. Melniker wrote:

"On July 3 I started treating Mr. Van Rosen, at which time he demonstrated right facial weakness, marked weakness of the right upper extremity, especially of the muscles of the wrist, hand and fingers. There was evidence of cog-wheel phenomena on extension of the wrist and supination of the forearm. There was also present a painful shoulder syndrome which appeared most marked upon extension of the wrist. The right lower extremity demonstrated some weakness. However, no muscle group appeared to test weaker than Fair plus. . . .

"However, the patient's condition worsened over the weekend and on the night of July 6 there was a great increase in pain and a marked flaccidity of the musculature of the entire right arm, the muscles of the wrist and hand testing Trace plus and Poor minus, the extensors and the flexors testing Fair to Fair minus and the muscles of the shoulder joint testing Trace minus to Trace plus. . . ."

Mr. Melniker tested me thoroughly, it now being about one and a half years since he'd last seen me. He was amazed at how much progress I had made. In his new report, May 8, 1962, he wrote:

"On examination today it was found that Mr. Van Rosen had complete range of motion and strength of normal level in the ankle joint. His strength and range of motion in the movements of hip flexion, adduction and abduction are Good plus. Range of motion and strength of hip rotation is slightly less strong.

"Movements of head and trunk flexion and head and trunk extension are normal, both in strength and range of motion. Range of motion in all joints of the right upper extremity is adequate and the strength functional. There is some limitation of range of motion in pronation and supination of the forearm.

"The main difficulty in the use of the upper extremity is in lack of fine coordination. There is occasional clonus in the fingers of the right hand when attempting small hand activities. Strength and range of motion of fingers appears to be adequate.

"The patient can roll in either direction from front to back; can raise to a quadruped position independently and from there rise to a standing position."

I was quite pleased when I read the report. That was, I thought, pretty good for a man who had twice been considered dying and of whom at least once it had been thought he would never walk again.

My first test in the Department of Speech Therapy had been taken November 13, 1959, given to me by Eleanor B. Morrison of that department. She gave me the Common Objects Test, adapted by Dr. Earl Chesher from the original test by Henry Head. It includes naming such objects as a key, pencil, spoon, matches, and the like, repeating the name of an object after the examiner, selecting an object on request, reading silently and then orally, and selecting an object from printed word. It also evaluates the flow of speech, pronunciation, the ability to repeat numbers and sentences, following written instructions to draw lines through circles and squares, writing to dictation, and the patient's general manner throughout the test. Finally, it involves reading a paragraph, perhaps from a newspaper, and then answering questions relating to the information in the paragraph.

I scored relatively well considering that it was only four months since I'd had my stroke. It showed, I think, what a good job Marcia had done working with me during that time. The report read:

"The patient was able to accurately name objects shown to him; repeat names of objects after the examiner; select objects on request; read printed names of objects aloud; select objects from the printed word.

"He was able to repeat sentences adequately. He repeated a three-digit number accurately but failed to repeat four- and five-digit numbers. Patient was able to execute oral commands, copy designs and execute written instructions. He cannot, however, write from dictation (i.e., key—plof; ten—sink; spoon—skof; pencil—

pilken). He recognizes his errors and says that although he knows it is wrong, he is unable to correct it.

"The patient is able to multiply three-digit numbers by three-digit numbers but is not able to verbalize the numbers or the process of multiplication.

"He is able to write his name and address with his nonparalyzed left hand.

"Mr. Van Rosen can read silently and answer questions (based upon the reading selection) accurately, but when he reads the same selection aloud he omits and substitutes words and phrases.

"The patient is able to understand the written and spoken word and appears to have little receptive language impairment.

"The patient's major impairment is one of expressive language, with greatest difficulties evident in verbalization of numerals and in expression through writing.

"His voice and speech abilities are generally adequate. Volume is adequate but fades at phrase ends. His pitch is appropriate but raises slightly with stress; rate is appropriate. Voice quality is breathy, throaty, flat and husky. His rhythm patterns are somewhat choppy and hesitant. Articulation, although generally good, becomes slack and blurred as patient's difficulty with verbalization becomes more severe. He has some difficulty in pronouncing some words and substitutes or inverts sounds (i.e., cavalry—calvary; birthday—girthday).

"Mr. Van Rosen was alert, pleasant and cooperative throughout the interview.

"Speech therapy is recommended."

When I went back in May, 1962, I was given the same tests by Mrs. Shirley Jackson and Dr. Jane Dorsey Zimmerman. The new report read:

"When seen for re-evaluation on 5/8/62 Mr. Van Rosen discussed his forthcoming projects of a book relating to his stroke and subsequent rehabilitation and the establishment of a fund to provide rehabilitation for other stroke victims. He was exceptionally fluent and spontaneous in his conversational speech.

"His use of receptive language skills remains good although his understanding of the spoken word is keener than that of the written word. Expressively, he shows improvement in conversational speech and in reading aloud. He continues to have some difficulty in repeating longer sentences and shows some slight perseveration. He cannot repeat combined number concepts, but he can repeat single-digit numbers. He can still write his name and address quite legibly with his left hand, but he continues to have difficulty writing from dictation. However, his spelling during this evaluation more nearly approached the phonetic spelling of words (comb—comp; spoon—spun; pencil—pent).

"His reading aloud was more accurate than previously with only an occasional word substitution which he does correct. He is able to find the answers to questions about the reading material but with some hesitation.

"Mr. Van Rosen's voice and speech characteristics show some improvement. Volume is now adequate and sustained. Pitch still rises with stress at times and there are some non-English patterns of intonation. Voice quality is still 'throaty,' tense and squeezed. Rate is now slow with somewhat choppy rhythm patterns. Articulation continues generally good, but still becomes blurred as patient's difficulty with verbalization becomes more severe; there is some dysarthria, distortion of sounds, omission or substitution.

"Mr. Van Rosen has a moderate conductive loss in the hearing of his left ear and a severe sensorineural loss for high frequencies. He says he has had this loss since he was a child.

"He reports that he has difficulty with words of more than two syllables and that speech and language are no easier for him in his native Russian.

"Continued speech therapy is not indicated at this time, particularly in view of the fact that Mr. Van Rosen feels he has gained as much benefit from therapy as is necessary for his pursuits."

I next stopped in at Occupational Therapy. As nearly as I can recall I was not originally tested in that department and since they could find nothing in the files my memory is probably correct. Here I was examined by Mrs. Flynn, who wrote:

". . . it was seen that even without past records for comparative reasons, this patient has done an extraordinary job of rehabilitating himself in attitude, outlook and general activities that for most patients would need the help, assistance and encouragement from the many therapies of rehabilitation. . . . It is obvious from his personal experiences and as a layman he is well motivated, oriented, organized and informed on the subject.

Functionally, the patient has a disabled right upper extremity but greatly improved in range of motion and muscle strength; and during his . . . re-education he encouraged the transfer to the left-hand dominance and therefore his right upper extremity is more an assistive limb. Of dominance in the dysfunction of this extremity is a lack of touch sensation. . . ."

From Occupational Therapy I went to see the Chief Psychologist (this was all in one day and kept me occupied for most of it), Dr. Manuel Riklan. He had also examined me in 1959, at which time he had written:

"This former packaging engineer evidently suffered a stroke some five months ago. He reports that immediately thereafter he developed weakness on the right side of the body and language difficulties. With the passing of time his motor functioning has returned to some degree. He reports that his main difficulties continue to be in expression including writing and language.

"On evaluation the patient was found to demonstrate a moderate degree of expressive aphasia including anomia. However, he appeared to comprehend adequately most of what was said to him. He was able to communicate in a fair manner. On the basis of psychological tests administered to the patient it would appear that no marked intellectual or thinking deficits are present. He seems to be currently functioning on an above level of intelligence and is capable, in non-verbal areas, of utilizing a high degree of integration and synthesis in his thinking processes. In dealing with verbal material of an intellectual nature, the patient's language distur-

75

bance interferes to a large degree with his responses, and
he, therefore, does rather poorly. It could be estimated
that at the present time, although the patient is functioning above average, this is somewhat below his basic
capacities.

"From the psychological point of view the patient
seems to demonstrate a mild type of reactive depression,
but appears to have a good deal of insight and understanding into the nature of his difficulties. From the
psychological point of view he can be considered a suit-
able candidate for a rehabilitation program. His primary
difficulties appear to be more in expression than in the
impairment of basic intellectual processes."

Dr. Riklan again examined me at some length on May
8, 1962, and his report read:

"On examination, the patient was found to be grossly
alert and oriented, although demonstrating some hesitation and slight confusion in certain instances. He continues to demonstrate language impairment, not so much
in spontaneous conversation, as when faced with specific problems and questions. There are impairments
also in his attention and concentration, as well as his
arithmetical and computational ability. On the other
hand, the patient is able to deal with non-verbal and abstract material in an adequate and intelligent manner.
On a simple visual motor test, he demonstrated the ability to integrate and organize his perceptions in an adequate manner.

"As compared with the findings of November, 1959,
certain improvements are apparent. His speech appears

to be more fluent and more functional. The patient appears capable of expressing most of his thoughts in an adequate manner. His thinking and associate reasoning, although still demonstrating some impairment, are quite adequate and can be judged as above average."

With a short break for a cup of coffee, I next went to the Daily Living Activities Department where I was tested by Mrs. Elton. There was no earlier test in this department, but this time Mrs. Elton reported:

"Mr. Van Rosen is remarkably independent in Activities of Daily Living. He uses his left hand for most activities but is able to assist himself with his right hand in some instances, for example in tying a tie. He dresses alone except for cuff buttons on left shirt sleeve. [This is not entirely accurate as I will show later. R.E.V.R.] His toilet activities are independent. Although he does not feel any sensation at all in his upper right extremity, he is able to grasp some objects and can for instance carry plates by holding them against his chest with the right upper extremity. The only great difficulty that he experiences is the fact that he cannot grasp a knife well enough in order to cut meat. He has learned to write with his left hand quite satisfactorily. He reports that he cooks and does his garden alone."

Accompanying this report were several sheets giving the evaluation on various activities. In bed activities, such as shifting position, sitting erect, procuring objects from a night table, turning on the light and adjusting covers, I was rated Good. All toilet activities Good. Washing and drying my face, brushing teeth, combing hair and shaving were also Good. Bathtub and shower activities were Good or Fair plus. In eating I drew a Good on everything except using my right hand in trying to cut meat. All dressing and undressing activities were rated Good. The same was true of the use of my left hand, except folding a letter and placing it in an envelope, striking a match, and winding my watch, on which I received Fair plus. Again it was Good on getting into and out of a bed and various kinds of chairs.

My last stop that day was in the office of Dr. Laszewski for a neurological examination. It served to confirm officially what the other reports had said. My physical condition had improved in every way, even to the slight use I could make of my right arm. My orientation was "adequate," intelligence "normal," attitude and insight "excellent."

I was tired but in good spirits when I left the hospital that day. I knew that I had been making progress but having it confirmed by the examinations at the hospital was a little like getting a diploma when you've graduated from school.

Despite this, I had no intention of sitting back and resting on my laurels. My disability was something I'd have to live with the rest of my life and I would always have to work to overcome it. I felt sure that there would always be progress if I continued to work at it. I'd had evidence of that only a few weeks before I went to the hospital for the new tests.

The floor of my terrace is about ten feet lower than the roof of the building. At the corner of the building there is a ladder leading to the roof. For a long time it had been a challenge to me and I had tried several times to climb it, with no success. Then one day in April I tried again and suddenly found I could do it. I had developed, through exercise, enough strength in my paralyzed arm so that I could hook my wrist over a rung of a ladder and hang on until I transferred my left hand to a higher rung.

There was more evidence a few months later in July. The Old Guard of the City of New York was having a pistol and rifle shooting match in Peekskill and I attended. I did not try, of course, to enter any of the regular matches but I did shoot a regulation round with my left hand (my actual score can be seen in Part III of this book.) I didn't do as well as I used to before my stroke but it was a beginning. Moreover, I was put in complete charge of the Old Guard Rifle Club pistol match and have successfully conducted the entire affair, issuing orders and commands for target shooting.

It was then a little more than three years since my stroke. It had been a painful period, not only physically but mentally, and it had been expensive. It had cost about $10,000. More than half of this had gone for doctors, nurses, and hospital expenses. Speech therapy had cost a little more than $400, and physical therapy slightly over $800. Drugs for the three years had run well over $1,000. Marcia and I were fortunate in that we had two insurance policies which paid part of the expenses—but only part. I'm not sure how we would have managed if we hadn't had the insurance.

In addition to this past expense, I can expect to pay

about $50 every month for daily drugs and a monthly visit to the doctor for the rest of my life.

But I have gained one valuable thing out of the last three years, besides the slow improvement. I cannot restore life and feeling to my right arm, nor can I completely cure the other damage caused by the stroke, but I do not have to give up doing useful work or abandon all the activities that gave me pleasure throughout most of my life. I do not have to be that useless cripple I imagined I was going to be the day I sat down and cried.

6. The Present

Stanley Cobb, writing about strokes, said: "This common neurological disorder is borne by some with courage and equanimity. Others are thrown into a deep depression. The variability of reaction is rarely a question of the type or location of the lesion but an expression of the whole life experience of the person who gets the stroke."

I'm sure that's true, not only about strokes but any disabling illness, and I feel that I am fortunate in having built my life around the belief that "if it's impossible I'll do it." I think it was that which first enabled me to overcome the depression when it did hit me, but I think there is more to it than that. I believe that a large part is played by knowledge about what has happened, what it involves, and complete information as to where and how to get help. I read all I could on the subject and Marcia and my sisters read much more. This furnished part of the knowledge; the rest came from experience in which

I learned, step by step, that there were other ways of doing things besides those I had been using all my life.

As this is being written (in September, 1962) I feel confident that I can have a rich and full life during my remaining years. My health is as good as can be expected. The blood clot which caused my stroke no longer represents a threat. It cannot be dissolved and there is no need to operate on it. The only real danger is another stroke, and that is being kept under control. I have a fairly long history of hypertension (what some people call "nerves") and high blood pressure. I have now shown that my blood tends to clot. Every day I take drugs to keep my blood pressure down, tranquilizers to keep me calm in moments of stress, and anticoagulants to prevent clotting. These three drugs make it fairly improbable that I will have another clot. I visit my doctor monthly so that he can check my condition and increase or decrease the dosages as required.

Since there is no sensation in my right arm and hand, I must be careful about injuring it. A cut would not be felt and I might not notice it until I had lost a dangerous amount of blood, since the anticoagulants might prevent normal clotting of the wound. I learned early to avoid accidents and hadn't had one until three months ago when I suffered a slight scratch. We soon noticed it, however, and a Band-Aid permitted it to heal.

There is always, of course, the possibility of an accident while walking or riding in a car or taxi. In case of a fairly serious accident, I would bleed to death much quicker than the average person. I carry at all times a card which tells what drugs I am getting so that, in case of accident, police and doctors will know what to do.

Physically there is only one small problem. My right leg functions only slightly below normal but even that slight degree can make it less trustworthy than the other leg. What happened to my right side has also brought about small changes in posture and balance. I've had a few falls—none serious. A couple of times I fell out of a chair at home. Once, on the street, although I was not dizzy, I found myself walking in a small circle and then fell. I sat for a few minutes, then took a taxi home. The danger of falling has, however, decreased with time and may now have completely vanished.

At present I am almost completely self-sufficient. This has been true for some time but my range of activities increases regularly.

Many months ago, Marcia, who had been working for a greeting-card publisher, decided to quit her job and free-lance. She felt that she could make as much or more money than she did on the job and she could work at home. I was delighted and was also determined to make it as easy for her as I could.

I do all the shopping for the house myself. If the bag isn't too large, I carry it home. If it is, I have it delivered. Marcia prepares breakfast and dinner, but at lunchtime I am the chef. I set the table, cook the food, and when everything is ready Marcia comes out of her workroom and we have lunch. At night, if we're having cocktails,

I mix and serve them. I have only two aids in these tasks. One is being sure that things are within easy reach. The other is an electric can opener.

There are many little things I can do around the house that also help. We have three cats, and I am responsible for cleaning and refilling their box. I can empty ash trays and help to tidy up in small ways. At night I get my own bed ready.

As the medical reports stated, I am capable of all my own toilet activities, including bathing, brushing my teeth, combing my hair, and so on. I don't need any special aids for these, although such things are available to those who need them.

By this time there are very few problems about dressing and undressing. Underwear, pants, socks and shoes are all easy to manage. I tie the shoelaces with one hand. There are two methods (these will be shown in Part III) but I prefer mine, which is easier and looks just as good. Putting on my shirt does represent a small problem but is easily solved. With shirts with button cuffs, Marcia moved the button on the left cuff so that it would be slightly looser than usual. I button that sleeve in advance, slip my arm through it and then go ahead. With French cuffs, I put the cuff links in before I start and proceed the same way. The only real problem is getting the shirt off. Then, I need someone to unbutton the left cuff; the rest I can do myself.

In the house, there are many things to keep me busy. I have a work desk and a set of files, with all my business and legal matters. I cover the current matters almost daily. I usually make several phone calls, personal and business. I have no trouble dialing. I may not be able to tell someone else a number, nor can I always remember a phone number, but I can see and dial the number. Since I cannot always remember my own address and phone number I always carry a piece of paper on which they are typed in words, not numbers. I can look at that and read it to someone on the phone or to a taxi driver.

During the summer the terrace keeps me well occupied. As I've mentioned, we have many flowers, including a hundred and twenty annuals that bloom every spring; shrubs, vegetables, and the two fruit trees. I make sure that they have plenty of plant food and water, and I also do simple pruning. All seem to be thriving. The first year we bought the peach tree, four years ago, our total crop was a solitary peach. Now we harvest over a hundred. Our cherry tree has also thrived and each year we usually get a few cherry pies as well as a supply for the fruit bowl.

Minor electrical repairs fall into my province, to about the same degree as with the average householder. I do all the minor carpentry. Since we have the terrace this is more than would occur in the average apartment. I can use a saw with my left hand, holding the board steady with my foot. Ordinarily in driving a nail I press the nail into the wood firmly enough to hold it, give it a light tap with the hammer, then drive it in. If I have any trouble I have a hammer with a magnetized head to hold the nail until I get it started. I also have a magnetized screwdriver which enables me to put screws in with one hand.

If I feel like watching television I have a comfortable, adjustable chair in front of the set. To avoid jumping up and down to switch channels, I have a remote-control switch at hand.

In the beginning, one of the things that gave me difficulty was winding my watch. I solved this by getting a self-winding watch so that the movement of my arm keeps it wound. Since I still wear it on my left arm, I use an expansion band. When I want to take it off, I can hook the fingers of my right hand under the band and then merely pull my left hand through it.

Afternoons, while Marcia is working, I quite often go out alone if there is nothing to do indoors. I knot my own tie, put on my coat, and overcoat in cold weather, and so on. I make sure that my change, wallet, handkerchief, and card case are all where I can easily reach them with my left hand. For my identification cards, membership cards, hospitalization cards, I use a case which opens like a waterfall, displaying all of them at once. That way, I can pull it from my pocket and open it all with the same motion and then indicate whichever card I need to show.

Before my stroke I enjoyed swimming. Since it is also good exercise, I was encouraged to try it again, and in the summer of 1960 I did. I have been going twice a week since. At first I could swim only on my side and that with difficulty, but within the past few months I've been doing the crawl once more. It may not be as good as I once did it but it propels me through the water and I've regained at least part of another pleasure.

Last summer I took a few dancing lessons, enough to convince me that I will be able to dance again—perhaps not the twist but at least the more conservative dances. I gave up the lessons chiefly because I didn't like the method of teaching rather than because of difficulties.

I often go out for a walk. I enjoy walking and it is also of great help in keeping the muscle strength of my right leg somewhere near where it should be. I have walked as much as five miles in one day.

Other times I go to an afternoon movie. I've always enjoyed motion pictures and, like television, they are much easier for me to follow than a novel or short story.

As you can see, I've learned to live a fairly normal life in spite of my disability. But the physical improvements, the learning how to surmount obstacles and to accomplish things in entirely new ways, are only part of the story. Just as important is the change in attitude which has taken place during the last three years. I've learned not to be thrown for a complete loss by the daily frustrations. Things that once would have thrown me into a complete rage still anger me but not to the point of threatening my health or my ability to cope with them. While it is true that the drugs have helped, they are not entirely responsible for the change.

The disability itself, the awareness that no magic can make it vanish, has taught me the elements of patience. When it takes you three years to learn to climb a short ladder you begin to realize that if things aren't done right the first try, or overnight, perhaps they will be done right the fifth, or the fiftieth, time. If nothing else, it saves a lot of wear and tear on the blood pressure and heart.

For the first time since that June day in Connecticut in 1959, I am full of plans and feel I have the strength and ability to turn them into reality. This book was the first plan to mature—but there are others, as you will see, in the process.

It's been a long way from Kiev and the Russian Revolution to the present. I can honestly say that I've enjoyed most of it and found it worthwhile. I have lived a full life and the defeats and illnesses are part of that fullness. Men can be defeated by anything—loss of money, loss of a job, loss of a loved one, loss of health or even the ability to grasp something—but men can also overcome anything. History furnishes many examples to prove this. As long as I remember this I still have a full life ahead of me and I can still say:

"If it's impossible I'll do it."

7. The Future

Several months before this book was accepted for publication, as I've mentioned, there was friction within my company, The Robert E. Van Rosen Corporation. The two persons who had taken over the operation had failed to make many of the payments called for in the contract. So far as tangible results were concerned, they had made no progress. Every board meeting turned into a futile argument, so Marcia and I finally resigned as members of the board. We still retained our controlling interest of stock.

The situation had not improved during the intervening months. They were making no sales and yet were running up grand expense accounts, mostly of long-distance personal phone calls and the costs of traveling around the country. I had no idea where this money was coming from but I did think that it partly explained why I was getting no payments.

Worse was still to come. Since the corporation bears

my name, I began to get phone calls from various businesses where they had incurred debts and never paid them. This was doing considerable damage to my credit standing. Something had to be done.

In the old days I might have suffered illness because of this situation—even another stroke—but now I decided to tackle the problem head on. I went to see my lawyer and we discussed the matter. It seemed to both of us that the corporation was being kept alive for only one reason and that was to put out a public stock issue which could enrich the corporation without necessarily giving anything to the purchasers of stock. Though I was the majority stockholder, I no longer had a vote on the board of directors so it did not mean that I would get any of the money. Still, it would be done in my name and would damage the one thing I had spent a lifetime building up in the business world.

There was only one thing to do, especially since it was impossible to locate either of the persons to discuss it. They were never in the office. We could reach only their attorney, who never knew where they were. During these discussions I also learned that they had issued corporation checks which were returned for insufficient funds. We immediately instituted a suit.

The case has not yet come to trial or settlement but I have no doubt that it will end with the recovery of my invention. When that is accomplished, I intend to reorganize the business and put it on the right road. Three and a half years have already been lost and more will be.

I know that the Comparator can perform a great service for every industry that advertises, whether it be through mass media or the package or label for their product, and this has already been proved to the heads of many large corporations. I am sure it has not moved ahead for two reasons: The machine was not properly presented, if at all; and the fact that industry does not like to do business with a company that appears unstable.

I will not be able to do everything myself, nor will I try. It is a valuable enough product that I should have no problem getting competent people to do the necessary work under my direction. And this time I will not make the mistake, committed through eagerness to get the business under way, of losing control of it.

What especially bothered me, when I realized I would not recover the use of my right arm, was that I no longer could follow my profession. Most of my work had involved art, all of it done with the right hand, but in the last few years before the stroke I had become one of the leading package designers in the country. It had been a rewarding profession in many ways and I had enjoyed the challenge. I simply could not accept the idea of never being able to practice it again.

Now I know that I don't have to abandon that either. What carried me ahead in the business was not my right hand; it was the work that went on in my mind. The designs that won me my awards were ideas; assembling them was merely a matter of following ideas.

I have recently started collaborating with a young man who has had experience in the field and has ideas of his own. He understands the profession well enough to translate the ideas I have and before long I expect you will once more see Van Rosen package designs in your favorite stores.

In addition to these, I have a new project which excites me very much. It stems directly from my illness. I have already mentioned that stroke is the Number Three killer in the United States yet less is known or done about it than almost any other ailment. I've related my own difficulty in learning how to help myself. I began to imagine how much worse it must be for persons living in areas not easily accessible to large hospitals and clinics, libraries, and bookstores.

Since then I've heard of a man in upstate New York who suffered a stroke about when I had mine. Three years later he could speak just a few words and was able to get around only with the aid of a cane. He had never had physical or speech therapy because his family didn't know there was any available. Apparently his doctor didn't know either. Yet this man lives only five miles from a town where he could have got such treatment and only sixty miles from New York City where there are hospitals devoted solely to rehabilitation. This case can be multiplied by many thousands.

Why should this be so? Why hasn't someone done something about it? I've asked these two questions everywhere I went. It seemed that strokes are a subject very much like the weather. Everyone talks about it but nobody does anything.

I suppose, in the beginning, my indignation was primarily for myself. I wanted help and information that I couldn't get. But gradually my indignation spread to cover everyone in the same predicament. We are the wealthiest nation in the world. We spend millions of dollars a year on research on cancer, heart disease, polio, and dozens of other diseases—as we should. But we spend almost nothing on investigating the stroke. Hundreds of thousands of people die each year, and more hundreds of thousands are maimed, yet the stroke remains the stepchild of medical research.

Many months ago I decided to do something about it as soon as I could. That time has also come.

Recently I put through the legal papers establishing The Foundation for Stroke Rehabilitation and Research, Inc. It is a nonprofit corporation sanctioned by the laws of New York State. I am now in the process of setting up a board of directors consisting of business and social leaders throughout the United States. Once that is accomplished, competent fund raisers will be employed and we will be under way. I intend to contribute as much of my time as I can and to be on hand to make certain that the foundation follows its original purpose and that large percentages are not milked off for "expenses."

I have talked to a number of doctors about the foundation; all of them have been enthusiastic. As I envision it, one of the things we will do is locate doctors throughout the country who are interested in stroke research and offer grants so that they can devote some of their time to such work. I believe, from what reading I've done, that there are many doctors who can contribute valuable work in the field if enabled to do so without too great a sacrifice. A few years of this and I'm sure an important breakthrough can be made in preventing strokes and in maintaining a higher degree of recovery in these cases. Soon, we hope, we will build a research center where many doctors can work together, besides those who work independently.

We will provide scholarships for men and women who are interested in physical or speech therapy. There will be only one condition attached to these scholarships. For the first two years of practice they must agree to practice in an area designated by us. Afterward they may remain or go wherever they like. We believe that this will quickly increase the number of therapists.

We will provide money for hospitals wishing to build or enlarge rehabilitation and therapy departments. While such facilities are now available in the largest cities, more are needed, and there are hundreds of smaller cities that have nothing to offer in this field.

We will see to it that every doctor and hospital in the country has information on what now exists and where it is available. To the best of our ability we will educate the lay public as to where to look if a stroke should strike them or someone close to them. And we will try to educate them to the fact that a stroke need not mean a lifetime spent in a bed or a wheel chair, speechless and helpless. The surviving stroke victim can be a completely functional person, capable of a full life and of providing for his family.

I am convinced that this foundation can soon help cut down the death rate from strokes—contrary to most illnesses, the death rate from strokes is increasing—and within a few years make possible the rehabilitation of more stroke victims than ever before. We are not so rich a nation that we can afford to toss people aside while so much can be done for them.

I am also convinced that within several years we can help to advance the knowledge about strokes so that a high percentage of them can be avoided. While doctors are not in total accord, there are many who believe that strokes occur only in certain types of personalities and that there are ways of recognizing the susceptible persons. If this is so, then research should eventually provide ways of detecting a potential stroke victim and the medical steps to guarantee that he remains only potential.

As for myself, I shall continue as always to try to improve my speech and my physical condition. I have no doubt that I shall go on making progress. I shall continue to enjoy my garden, my walk, swimming and shooting, and my home and social life—able once again to enjoy being busy.

There is one aspect of my life which I have left out, feeling that it was more appropriate for the end of this chapter. That is the spiritual side.

When I was a child in Russia I attended both the Russian Orthodox and Lutheran churches, then drifted away from church for a time. For several years I was a Christian Scientist, but a few years ago when I was in the

Middle West we joined and always attended the Episcopal church.

Shortly after I was able to go out, following my stroke, I went for a Sunday walk and suddenly felt the desire to go to church. There is an Episcopal church near our apartment and I dropped in for the services. Afterward I remained to meet the pastor. Since then I have gone every Sunday. It has helped me greatly during the past three years.

When I was asked exactly how it had helped, what I felt that it gave me, I first replied that I felt relieved after a religious experience such as praying and that I felt better believing that there was a Power that is not as vulnerable as Man. But even as I gave it I knew that this wasn't the precise answer. I thought about it that night, and the next day I had the answer. I said:

"Going to church cauterizes what has happened to me."

PART II

"In the treatment of apoplexy the doctor's skill is not enough. Patients must have an understanding of their strokes and what happens to them if they are to achieve the best possible recovery. Awareness is needed because an essential ingredient in that recovery is their own determination to win it, their own willingness to work for it patiently and intelligently. It is just as important that this knowledge be shared by those members of the family who help care for the patient and are closest to him. Those who realize that they are not necessarily in a hopeless state, and whose families realize it too, often can be restored to happy useful lives."

IRVINE H. PAGE, M.D., *Strokes,* (Dutton, 1961)

8. "His Fire Is Out"

—(JONATHAN SWIFT)

The history of apoplexy, or stroke, is a long one—and almost as vague as it is long. We know that it is mentioned in ancient references. The treatment, such as it was, consisted of bleeding the patient (there are rare cases today where that is still recommended) at regular intervals. It probably did no more harm than anything else they might have tried at the time.

Jonathan Swift had a stroke when he was almost seventy. He recovered, but there must have been some permanent damage, for three years later he wrote, referring to himself, the poem which includes the line: "His fire is out, his wit decay'd." There are many persons, I'm sure, who have never had a stroke and wish that their wit was no more decayed than Swift's. No doubt Swift's mind was impaired in his later years, and this was probably the result of the stroke rather than insanity, as many writers have stated.

It wasn't until 1842 that Rowland East, an English authority, maintained that apoplexy was one of the two most dangerous diseases in Britain.

Our own Walt Whitman had five strokes between the ages of thirty-nine and sixty-eight, two of which left him partly paralyzed. If not much is known about strokes today, far less was known then; but Whitman's paralysis left him each time and he lived to the ripe old age of seventy-three, when he died of tuberculosis.

Robert Louis Stevenson, on the other hand, suffered from tuberculosis all of his life, then had his first stroke and died in his middle forties.

Although statistics are not available, there can be no doubt that the death rate from stroke was very high in the past. Despite this, quite a few famous men had strokes and survived to continue their work. Louis Pasteur was one, and he did most of his work after his stroke.

A famous English surgeon suffered a stroke which left his right arm permanently impaired. Slowly, painfully, he taught himself to use his left hand and developed the muscles in the right hand so that it could hold instruments. Within a relatively short time he was performing delicate operations as well with his left hand as he once had with the right.

The most famous case of stroke in our own country was probably that of President Woodrow Wilson. He was traveling over the country trying to get popular support for our entry into the League of Nations when the stroke occurred. He lived for several years afterward but he never fully recovered. Many persons like to speculate on how much Wilson's stroke influenced our history—or even that of the world—during the past forty years.

More recently, President Dwight D. Eisenhower suffered a stroke following his heart attack, but recovered to carry on as well as before. Shortly after leaving office, Sir Winston Churchill also had a stroke but apparently recovered completely. And still more recently Joseph Kennedy, father of our President, had a stroke but seems to be getting over it at a normal speed.

Some, of course, never made it. Catherine the Great, of Russia, died of a stroke. Physicians have speculated on how often the history of the world is influenced by men and women with arteriosclerosis (hardening of the arteries) and how different events might be if this weren't so.

9. The Story of Strokes

It is not so many years since people believed, despite the few who fully recovered, that a stroke meant the end of the person's life. It was essentially true, for those who did not die survived as semi- or lifelong invalids. Little was known about strokes and there was practically nothing to do for those who were afflicted. Even less was known about methods of rehabilitation. What little progress has been made happened within the last ten or fifteen years. The first conference in his country on cerebral vascular disease was held as late as 1954.

While the big breakthrough has been with drugs—especially the anticoagulants and tranquilizers—there have also been advances in knowledge about strokes. More progress has been made in the last dozen years than in all previous time.

In simple terms, a stroke, or cerebral vascular accident, means that something happens which deprives a part of the brain of its normal supply of blood. This results in temporary or permanent damage to the brain and to those parts whose function is controlled by that particular section of the brain. As mentioned earlier, there are three major kinds of strokes.

Victims of all three kinds usually have a few physical aspects in common. They nearly always have hypertension or high blood pressure. Often they are overweight. And all doctors believe that they have arteriosclerosis to some degree.

Arteriosclerosis, or hardening of the arteries, is a condition brought about by deposits of fat and/or calcium in the arteries. The leading offender, however, is fat or cholesterol, a substance manufactured by our bodies from animal fats. This has brought about a medical debate which is still going on. One group of doctors believes that cholesterol is the causative factor in both strokes and heart disease and that we must all find diets containing as little animal fat as possible, replacing them with the fats or oils from vegetables and fish. In support of their argument they cite the statistics on heart disease and stroke in such countries as Japan and India where there is almost no animal fat in the diet.

The opposing group, which seems to be growing at the moment, admits that Americans have a higher cholesterol count than people of other nations and many of them agree that the condition brought about by this may make it easier for the arteries to be obstructed. But that's as far as they will go. They deny that this is caused by animal fats and point out that in controlled experiments some people on a diet with the lowest possible content of animal fat have produced more cholesterol in their bodies than those who ate all the animal fat they wanted. Recently they have cited the results of other experiments showing that an individual's cholesterol count may vary according to the emotional climate, climbing much higher when the person is tense. Neither side has yet had a clear-cut victory and it will be up to future research to decide.

Whatever the cause, fat and calcium do stick to the walls of the arteries and in time harden. More of it comes along to cling and harden so that the walls of the arteries become thicker and there is less space for the passage of blood. This makes it easier for a clot to stop the flow of blood. It may even contribute more than that, for there are some doctors who believe that fragments of this superimposed wall break off to form clots.

It is generally believed that arteriosclerosis is a disease of the old, but this is only partly true. Doctors say that every older person has arteriosclerosis to some extent. However, it has been discovered in many young people and even in babies. Obviously, everyone with arteriosclerosis does not get a heart attack or a stroke. It seems to me—although I don't know how many doctors will agree with me—that this indicates that arteriosclerosis may be a contributing factor rather than the cause of stroke.

The most common of the three kinds of stroke is that caused by a blood clot in an artery leading to the brain. No one is quite sure how or why a clot forms, but the leading theories on this have already been outlined

A view of one end of my terrace, showing part of my minia-
ture farm on which I'm the only farmer.

This was one of my early attempts to write and was done September 24, 1959, before I went to Hunter College. The bottom half, which is mostly scrawls, was an attempt to write with my right hand. I soon gave this up and concentrated on using my left.

This was written November 20, 1959, still before I had gone to Hunter College, but it already shows considerable improvement over the work I did in September. As you can see, it took me twenty-two minutes to do this one page.

Here's a sample of my writing on February 5, 1960, just after I started therapy at Hunter College. It took me twenty-five minutes to complete this page.

```
7:05                February 5th   ©
A.M.
m  7 5 2 9 6 34 11 8 10 9 2
p  5 7    6 7 34 10 13 2 18 11 6
         OR-5-4581
         GR-9-2453
         AL-5-8954
         CL-6-0560
   paper. paper. paper. paper
   paper.
   apple. apple. apple. apper.
   apple. apple.
   puppy. puppy. puppy. burppy
   puppy. Papers have news.
   Apples some times have worms
                         7:30
```

```
Write each word 5x.      ⓓ

like like like like like like

light light light light light
                          light
line line line line line line

lime lime lime lime lime lime

lie lie lie lie lie lie

m V.R. does best First 15 minutes
2 - 15 minute sessions as you have
been doing - is good. Good lesson today

Practice naming numbers -10-20
```

This was done March 4, 1960. The top line, the first word in each line of words, and the comment at the bottom were written by my therapist.

```
        April 25th    7:16  ⓔ
 6  12 9 11 17 5 14 10   A.M.
 20 13 8 6 2 15 9 6 16 17 5 11
 14 10 21 3 18. 6 2 11 9 7 5
 10 4 1 3 8 14 13 18 15 12
 sing sing sing
 bring bring  bring
 coming coming coming
 going going going
 walking walking walking
 talking talking talking
 eating eating eating
 This girl is pretty.
 A kid is playing with paint.
                        7:35
                        A.M.
```

April 25, 1960. This was done in a comparatively short time and contains very few errors.

et 6/2/60 · June 3, 7:29 A.M.

k Write 2 sentences each
  day with __have__
  write 3x .

great great great great
+ I have great hopes for you.

grip grip grip grip
+ I have a strong grip in my
    right hand.
grade grade grade grade
+ We will have top-grade
                tomatoes.
grind grind grind grind

groom groom groom groom

grand grand grand grand

green green green green

Another exercise, this one on June 3, 1960. Only part of it is reproduced here, but it's enough to show progress. The instructions at top and each key word were written by the therapist.

July 13th 7:45

spoil spoil spoil spoil
grasp grasp grasp grasp
Spanish spanish spanish spanish

Some foods spoil easily in hot
            weather.
I do not grasp the significance
    of letter separation.

Spanish foods are very
        rich.

s)   8:00 A.M.

July 14th 7:23 A.M.

spine spine spine spine
speed speed speed speed
spell spell spell spell
    grasp clasp spoil spoke

This is my work on July 13, 1960, and part of my work on the following day.

police police police police
police police police police
police police police police
police police police police
police police police

diplomats
diplomats diplomats
diplomats diplomats
diplomats diplomats
diplomats
diplomats diplomats
diplomats diplomats

(H)

United (I) 100 %
United United United
united united
united United
united united united

Hunter
Hunter Hunter
Hunter Hunter Hunter
Hunter Hunter Hunter
Hunter Hunter Hunter
embassy
embassy embassy
embassy embassy
embassy embassy
embassy embassy
embassy embassy
embassy embassy

These two pages are part of work on October 13, 1960, shortly before I gave up the sessions at Hunter College. As you can see on the second page I was given 100% for this work. It was almost like getting a diploma.

This is a painting of mine, done several years ago, which was widely praised by art critics, including the critic for the New York *Times*.

Sep. 1961

You've already seen an example of my art work before I had
the stroke. These two drawings were made with my left hand
in September, 1961.

Feb. 12, 1962

Feb. 12, 1962

A few months later, February 12, 1962, I made these two
drawings which already show some improvement in the use
of my left hand.

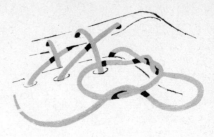

Put a knot in one end of lace, as shown, and readjust lace so that the knot is tight against inside of shoe.

Pull end of lace in under loop and then over, leaving another loop on the outside.

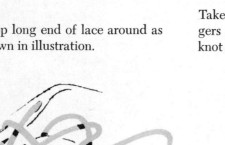

Loop long end of lace around as shown in illustration.

Take the outside loop in the fingers and pull so that it forms a knot with a single bow.

Run the long end of lace under the loop, then back over and back under to make a simple knot as illustrated.

Arrange bow as shown so that it is horizontal to the top of the show. It will now look like a perfectly normal knot.

I learned this method by reading *Stroke* by Douglas Ritchie, which is published in this country by Doubleday.

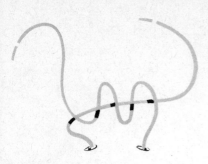

Drop lace A over the top of the shoe, then wrap lace B over it as shown here.

Tighten laces by pressing on lace A with the third finger and lace B with the thumb (if the left hand is being used it's just the opposite) and slide them in opposite directions.

Make a loop in lace B as shown, laying it across the top of the shoe, then throw lace A over it as above.

Now make a loop in lace A and pass it in under the loop in lace B. This forms a knot.

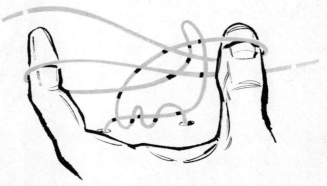

Tighten the knot by putting the thumb in one loop and the forefinger in the other and spreading them apart. This may seem difficult at first but a little practice will make it easy.

This is the method I learned at the hospital. It is a little more complicated than the other method.

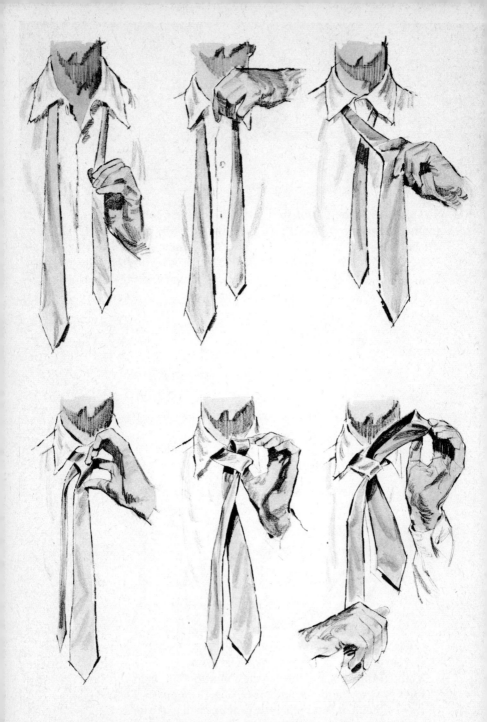

This method for making a four-in-hand is clear and easy to
follow. Even better, it is a simple way of knotting a tie.

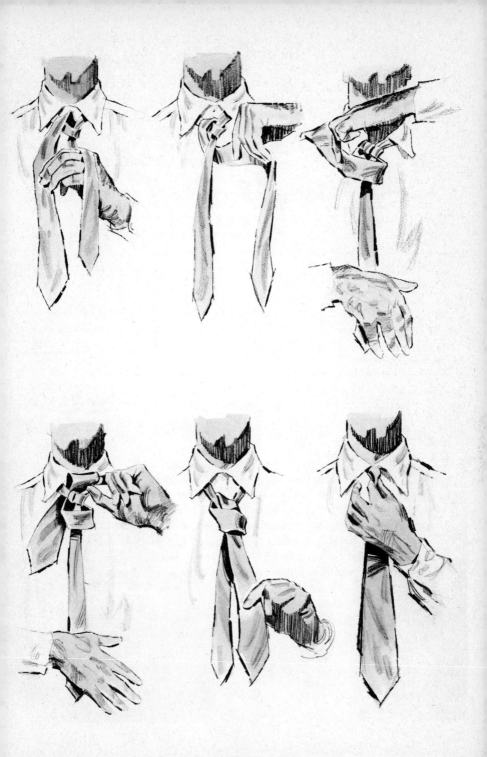

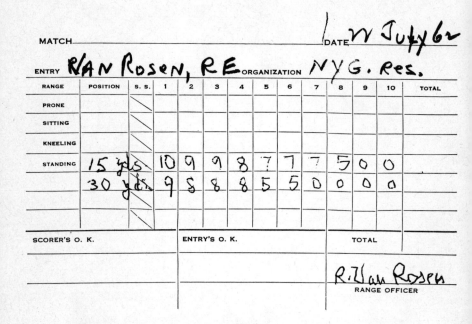

MATCH _____ DATE 1 W July 62

ENTRY **Van Rosen, R E** ORGANIZATION **N Y G. Res.**

RANGE	POSITION	S. S.	1	2	3	4	5	6	7	8	9	10	TOTAL
PRONE													
SITTING													
KNEELING													
STANDING	15 yds		10	9	9	8	7	7	7	5	0	0	
	30 yds		9	8	8	8	5	5	0	0	0	0	

SCORER'S O. K.   ENTRY'S O. K.   TOTAL

R. Van Rosen
RANGE OFFICER

This is an exact copy of my score in the Old Guard Rifle Club
Pistol match held at Camp Smith, Peekskill, New York, July
22, 1962. I was also the range officer for this, which was the
only pistol match held during the Old Guard's Annual Rifle
Matches. I think the scores show how well I've learned to use
my left hand but it also shows something else which is typical of the person who has had a stroke. Fatigue sets in much
quicker and it is illustrated here by the gradual lowering of
the score as I shot.

This is a photograph of me on the range during the Old Guard pistol match in July, 1962.

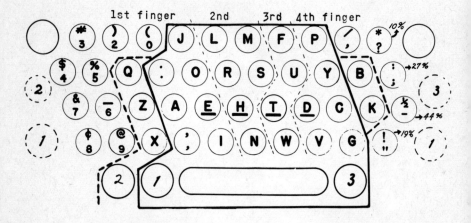

SIMPLIFIED ONE-HAND KEYBOARD FOR THE RIGHT HAND

Keys in area bounded by the solid line are easily reachable from the "Guide Keys"—E, H, T and D. These keys are used for 96.5% of ordinary typing. Keys in area bounded by the dotted lines, used for 2.5% of ordinary typing, can be reached by extended reaches of the first and fourth fingers without the hand leaving the "Guide Position." Thus 99% of ordinary typing can be done from one position over the "Guide Keys."

Key "1" at left end of shortened space bar is the location of the shift key, making it operable by the thumb while fingers strike the capital letters without movement of the hand from the "Guide Position." Key "2" at left of new shift key position is the new position of the shift lock key. Key "3" at right end of space bar is the location of the carriage-return key on Electromatic and Burroughs typewriters, enabling its operation by the little finger without leaving the "Guide Position."

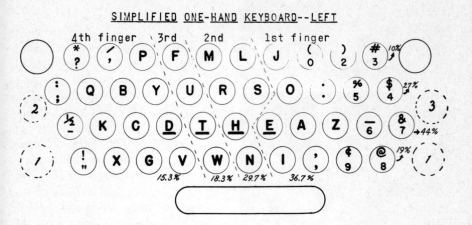

SIMPLIFIED ONE-HAND KEYBOARD FOR THE LEFT HAND

This is the keyboard for the person who must type left-handed. It is worked out on the same scientific basis as the right-handed keyboard. The percentages at the bottom indicate the frequency the letters in each section are used. Either of these keyboards can be installed on both manual and electric typewriters by the Tytell Typewriter Company. (Both photographs by courtesy of the Tytell Typewriter Co., Inc., 116 Fulton St., New York 38, N.Y.)

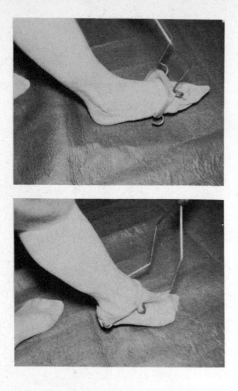

This is the device, mentioned in the book, which can be used to put on stockings with one hand. Notice how the stocking is rolled up almost to the toe in the first picture, then unrolls as it is pulled on the foot. Tilting the device, as in the second illustration, will pull the stocking over the heel. The stocking will continue to unroll as it is pulled up the leg. (Photographs by courtesy of Rehabilitation Services, Inc., 204 Court Street, Binghamton, N.Y.)

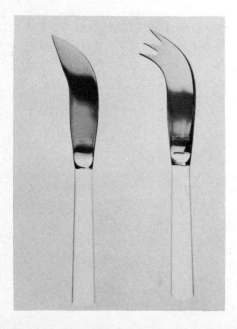

Two examples of a knife to be used with one hand. The one on the bottom is a combination knife and fork while the other is only a knife. The curved shape of the knife makes it easier to cut food by using a rocking motion, eliminating the need to hold the food down with a fork while cutting it. The blades are stainless steel and the handles are ivory grained celluloid. (These are sold by The Winkley Company, 1330 Washington Avenue North, Minneapolis 11, Minnesota; Photograph by courtesy of the manufacturer, Lamson & Goodnow Mfg. Co., Shelburne Falls, Massachusetts.)

above. The clot moves along in the blood stream until it reaches a spot where the passage is too narrow for it to continue. There it lodges, shutting off the flow of blood to some section of the brain, and a stroke occurs.

There is no way to anticipate how much damage may be done when this happens. Most sections of the brain receive blood from more than one source, the amount from the different sources varying with each individual. Therefore a clot in the carotid artery of the neck (as in my case) of one person may result in damage to a large portion of the brain, while another person might have a similar clot yet suffer little or no brain damage. This is one reason why doctors emphasize the fact that strokes differ.

Embolism can also cause a stroke and may or may not be a blood clot, but since it is so similar in every way I include it with the first kind of stroke. An embolism is caused by the introduction of a foreign substance into the blood stream. If a drop of oil were injected into a vein, a fatal embolism would result. This often happens in severe accidents when some of the body fat is forced into a torn vein. But, here, we are more concerned with the "normal" ways it can happen.

An embolism might be caused by a cluster of bacteria, a fragment of tumor tissue, or a particle of blood clot breaking off from a diseased spot in the body. When such a particle has entered the blood stream it may travel anywhere. It may lodge in a leg artery, resulting merely in some difficulty in walking. It may go to the heart, or lung, causing trouble there; or it may travel toward the brain, causing a stroke. Fortunately, this accounts for a very small percentage of strokes and is decreasing with modern methods of treatment.

Another cause of stroke, which does not involve a clot but produces the same result, is a spasm in the artery wall. This causes the artery to close and the flow of blood to the brain is shut off just as effectively as if by a clot.

The second kind of stroke is, in a way, controversial, since many doctors claim that it isn't a stroke. But I include it because the results are the same and are brought about in pretty much the same fashion. It involves a brain tumor which grows and presses against a blood vessel until finally the pressure cuts off the flow of blood. Deprived of its food, a section of the brain reacts exactly as in the case of a clot.

The third kind is due to brain hemorrhage. When this occurs the patient almost always has a history of high blood pressure and hypertension. I do not mean that high blood pressure will cause a hemorrhage but it is an important contributing factor, once other conditions make a ruptured artery or vessel possible. There are many causes of brain hemorrhage, although the results are usually much the same.

Most of the blood vessels feeding the brain are known as small arteries. Like the arteries, they are subject to an accumulation of fat along the walls—but here the outcome is different. As the walls thicken with fat and scars, small hemorrhages occur within the vessel and after a time these serve to weaken the walls. Eventually, especially if the individual has high blood pressure, a rupture may occur, flooding the brain with blood. The result is a stroke.

Another cause is an aneurysm, or a blister, on the wall of the artery. These blisters bulge like a weak spot in a balloon and indicate a dangerously thin wall. The blister usually enlarges with age, further weakening the wall, and a rupture may result at any time. This condition is often found in an individual at birth; such hemorrhages often occur in children and the young.

Occasionally, for reasons not known, nature makes a few mistakes in fashioning an individual. The normal course for blood is to leave the heart, enter the large arteries, which then branch off into smaller ones until finally the blood enters the little arteries. From there it enters the capillaries. During this trip it delivers food and oxygen and picks up wastes. Once through the capillaries, the blood enters small veins and proceeds to carry off the waste products. At times this process fails to develop in a normal fashion and blood may be pumped directly from an artery into a vein, with no opportunity to perform its function, and thus enters the vein under too much pressure, not having the chance to slow down.

Veins are not constructed to withstand as much pressure as arteries, so when this occurs the walls of the vein expand and stretch thin. Sooner or later the walls can stretch no further and then they tear, releasing the blood into the brain to cause a stroke.

A hemorrhage may also result from disease in other parts of the body. This happens when a particle of an infected organ breaks loose and gets into the blood stream. It attaches itself to the vessel wall, and soon the wall is weakened enough to rupture.

These, then, are the causes of strokes. I have condensed the story—books have been written on the subject—but the essential facts are here. I have included the things that are known but I haven't mentioned the things that are unknown—and they are many. Much progress has been made in the last decade—enough to show how much there still is to accomplish. And this calls for more money, more people working on the project, and more facilities.

In 1958, the last year for which we have figures, 190,758 persons died from strokes. More than 500,000 more suffered some impairment and disability from strokes. Only heart disease and cancer show higher figures. What have we done about it?

It is estimated that $17,808,259 of federal monies is spent in a year on medical research. Of this, only $1,351,540 was allocated to specific research in cerebral vascular diseases. While we were spending $17 million on medical research for American citizens, we spent $189,820,000 on research on farm animals—or almost twelve times as much. And during the same period of time the American people spent $116,790,000 for face creams, $84,220,000 for toilet water and cologne, and $31,120,000 for nail polish and enamel.*

"In the United States, however, central nervous system vascular lesions have not attracted their propor-

---

* These figures were obtained from a fact sheet compiled by the National Health Education Committee, Inc.

tional share of interest and research funds as have heart disease and cancer. No voluntary agency has cerebro-vascular accidents as its primary health problem."**

** Charles M. Wylie, M.D., in the *Journal of Chronic Diseases,* August 1961.

10. The Warning Signals

As I said earlier, the personality and emotional environment of the individual is closely linked to the onset of a stroke and the rehabilitation that follows. All too little research has been done in this area, but most doctors are in agreement about the relationship, and more and more studies are being made. The wise doctor knows that emotional factors must be considered in the treatment of many physical ailments but in some instances they are of greater importance than in others. It is believed that stroke is one of these.

Most men, Thoreau said many years ago, lead lives of quiet desperation. This is even truer today. The average man or woman today is constantly beset by worries. These start in the home with anxieties about meeting the rising cost of living, about keeping up life and medical insurance, about the health and welfare of loved ones, about saving money against the day that work may be impossible, and sometimes about just meeting day-to-day expenses. From the home, anxieties spread out to embrace such larger problems as the possibility of war and the use of the H-bomb. In between, there are dozens of worries that plague the average person.

It is significant that many writers have termed our period "The Age of Anxiety." It is still more significant that we have more people in psychoanalysis and more people in mental hospitals than ever before, and our consumption of tranquilizers staggers the imagination.

What does this have to do with strokes? Doctors know that anxieties, or tensions, are basic factors in hypertension and high blood pressure. More recently it has been proved that tension can change the cholesterol content of the blood, and it is believed that cholesterol has a direct bearing on the inroad of arteriosclerosis. As I have already pointed out, it is believed that hypertension, high blood pressure, and arteriosclerosis are basic causes of all strokes.

More knowledge in this field will undoubtedly one day lead to the prevention of many strokes. In the meantime, it can be an important factor to the doctor. This is especially true in the case of the "little stroke" the patient may experience one or more times before he suffers a serious stroke. The little stroke should be enough warning to the doctor—and to the patient—to take steps to prevent the serious attack. That is the time to get at the emotional roots, for everything that caused the little stroke is still present, along with the fear and anxiety about having another stroke. Sometimes this latter fear can cause more damage than the stroke which brought it into being.

An awareness of these factors can enable the patient to help himself in avoiding a stroke. Once he knows that he is prone to the underlying causes of a stroke, he can make frequent trips to the doctor so that his blood pressure can be kept at a normal level. If he knows that he is given to excessive anxiety and worry, he can discuss with his doctor the possibility of medication to see him through periods of stress.

An awareness of what is going on in his own body is just as important to the patient in preventing a stroke as it is to recovery. This cannot be overemphasized.

The idea that a stroke can be anticipated and therefore stopped before serious brain damage occurs is a new one, coming to the fore less than fifteen years ago. It is becoming accepted by more and more doctors and I believe it will be one of the major interests of future researchers.

The strokes caused by blood clots make up the largest percentage of all. And of these about 75 per cent are caused by a clot in the carotid system (that is, a clot in a neck artery). In a way, this is fortunate, for it is easiest to anticipate this kind of stroke by typical warning signals. These warnings are actually the little or mild strokes I have already mentioned. A person may have one little stroke which is eventually followed by a major stroke, while another person may have a dozen little strokes without ever experiencing anything worse. But the important thing is that a warning is given and the doctor has an opportunity, if the patient goes to see him when the warning occurs, to fight the serious stroke before it happens.

When a little stroke strikes a person it means that there is a temporary lack of blood in some region of the brain. Although the symptoms will last only a few seconds or minutes, they will be very similar to the first reactions to a permanent block in an artery.

Each half of the body is controlled by the opposite half of the brain. In other words, if you are a right-handed person your right side is controlled by the left half of your brain, which is called dominant. It also controls your use of language, whether speaking and writing or understanding what others say or write.

So the right-handed person, having a temporary blockage in a left artery, suddenly experiences a weakness on his right side. There may also be numbness and a pricking sensation and sometimes an inability to move the leg and arm in a normal fashion. The feeling might be similar to what happens when a person's legs have been crossed too long and a pinched nerve causes one leg to "go to sleep," but a larger area will be affected in the case of an incipient stroke and the two symptoms should not be confused.

There may be a lack of control of the right side of the mouth, and speech may be slurred if the patient tries to talk during the attack. Dizziness may occur if the patient tries to walk. There may also be impairment of vision. The patient may not see objects to his right, when staring directly ahead, if the left artery is involved; or he may have double vision.

In the event that the blockage of the artery affects the entire carotid system, the person will probably experience all of the above symptoms. If only a part of the system is deprived of blood, he may experience only one or a few of the symptoms. When it is a little stroke, it will be over in a few minutes, whereas in the more serious stroke the symptoms get worse in a series of steps. In either case, the person should see his doctor as soon as possible. Since doctors seldom have the chance to see the patient during the attack, the patient should tell the doctor in detail what happened to him. Many people fail to do this, or don't even see the doctor at all. The incident passes so quickly that they dismiss it from their minds. Some people also have such a fear of strokes that they prefer to avoid talking about symptoms.

Enough progress has been made in the treatment of strokes so that today a doctor can often prevent a major stroke, if he knows of a definite threat. But he cannot do this if the patient keeps secrets. He needs the patient's full cooperation so that the danger can be faced with awareness of the facts.

Fortunately, strokes from causes other than clots are not nearly so frequent, for they do not give as many advance warnings. In the case of hemorrhage in the brain there is no warning until the bleeding has already started. Then there may be a sudden and extremely painful headache and stiffness in the neck. The patient usually becomes unconscious soon after, although there are cases when this did not happen. The patient may also experience nausea and vomiting.

Migraine headaches often produce symptoms which the layman might confuse with those of a stroke. He will often have a weakness on one side, perhaps some dizziness or impairment of vision, followed by a sick headache. These signs are not, however, similar, and a physician can quickly detect the difference. For some unknown reason people given to migraine attacks seldom have strokes.

While I have stressed, as have many doctors, that information can be of great assistance to the patient, a warning goes with it. The symptoms described in this and other books on the subject are meant as a guide. The person who recognizes symptoms in himself, or in someone else, should immediately get in touch with a doctor so that a possible illness may be treated before it becomes serious. *Information should never be used by a person to diagnose his own illness.*

11. The First Attack

The beginning of a more serious stroke is usually termed an "advancing stroke" until the symptoms become less severe, when it is labeled a "completed stroke." Once that cycle is completed the damage is done and it is the job of the physician and the patient (and his family) to repair as much of the damage as possible and to try to insure that it doesn't happen again. To know when this point has been reached, the doctor may have to keep a close watch on the patient for several hours.

The period varies according to the cause of the stroke. If from an embolism, the stroke will probably be completed in less than a minute. If the cause is a hemorrhage, when the progression of symptoms has stopped and remains static for five or six hours, it may be assumed that it has done all the damage it is going to do. In the case of a stroke caused by a blood clot, if the progress of symptoms stops completely for about twenty-four hours it has probably reached the completed stage.

The beginning of the major stroke is similar to that

described for the little stroke. The difference is that in
the little stroke the symptoms last at most only a few
minutes, whereas in a major stroke they continue and
worsen in stages. A good example of this is given in the
description of my own symptoms early in this book.

I'd had many of the warning signals, although in my
case a thorough examination failed to show what was
actually happening. Then, on the day my wife and I
were going to the country, numbness began in my right
arm. This condition remained static for several hours,
when I suddenly was unable to use the arm. Again, a
few hours passed before another symptom appeared—
when my speech began to slur as we started home. This
time the interval was shorter, for by the time we had
reached home my speech was worse and I couldn't remember my own address when I phoned the doctor.

At this point the doctor should be able to know what
is happening by examining the patient in his own home.
But, despite the variance in symptoms, he cannot be
sure what kind of stroke it is. He can only guess—until
he gets the patient to a hospital for observation and
specific tests.

On his way to the hospital the patient will probably
be in one of two moods. He may believe that it's nothing
serious, as I did, and feel only irritation about the im-
pending confinement; or he may be frightened because
he knows only old wives' tales about the horrors of
strokes. Of the two, I suppose the former is preferable
for that period—although, as I know so well, it can sometimes lead to a rude shock later.

What happens when the patient first reaches the hospital will depend on the patient's general condition and further observations by the doctor. He must now try to complete his diagnosis as quickly as possible, for he has a double job ahead of him. He must treat the present stroke and try to avoid another stroke, which sometimes follows close upon the first.

If conditions warrant, he will have certain tests made. An examination of the cerebro-spinal fluid may determine if there has been a hemorrhage, for in about 85 per cent of strokes from bleeding in the brain some blood will be found in the spinal fluid.

Differences in symptoms in the causes of strokes are not enough in this case. Other conditions might confuse the symptoms. If the stroke is caused by a clot, the doctor may want to administer anticoagulants, which might dissolve the clot and prevent others from forming; but if he's made a wrong guess and the cause is bleeding, this would be the wrong medication. So the testing of the spinal fluid is an important step.

Depending on his examination and observation, the doctor may decide that surgery is the best weapon against the stroke—necessary especially in the presence of blood clots. When this is required, the surgeon reaches the affected vein and ties it off, isolating the clot, and where possible letting other arteries bear the load of feeding the brain. In other cases, a section of artificial artery is put in to by-pass the clotted area. In either case, it is necessary to know the exact location of the clot. There is no way to discover this from the symptoms or from observation.

Normally, internal observations are made by X ray, but veins and arteries do not show in an X-ray picture. Occasionally arteriosclerosis will be so advanced that the heavily lined wall of an artery will cast a slight shadow, no more.

Several years ago a process was discovered by which pictures, called arteriograms or angiograms, can be taken of veins and arteries. It involves the injection of a dye into a neck artery which will show up on an X-ray plate as it is carried along by the blood stream. In that way a clot can be located. For several years, however, this method was used sparingly, for there were many bad side effects and it is believed that a number of patients died as a result of it.

In more recent times there have been many improvements in the dye used and many doctors now believe that it is entirely safe. Reports from England state that in the past 50,000 occasions of its use there has been no harm to the patients. An American neurosurgeon, Dr. Robert A. Kuhn, has said: "It can be repeated, with complete assurance, that today the performance of cerebral arterial studies carries immeasurably less risk than that posed by the conditions for which it is used. Cerebral angiography is the bright hope of the future for the stroke victim."*

Sometime during this early period, the patient will usually seem to get better suddenly. This does not necessarily mean that some medication is performing mir-

* *New Hope for Stroke Victims,* by Robert A. Kuhn, M.D., Appleton-Century-Crofts, 1960.

acles, for it is a step that nearly always takes place in the advancing stroke. It lasts for a short time and then the patient takes a turn for the worse. This too is part of the pattern.

In any kind of stroke the first several days in the hospital are the critical ones. In my own case, there were ten days in which the doctors were not sure that I'd pull through. The patient's temperature may go up, sometimes quite high, and he may be incoherent or in a coma. This is the period when nurses may be needed around the clock and when the doctor must keep a close watch.

Fortunately, it doesn't last too long.

12. The House of Illness

None of us likes being in a hospital, but there is one thing about it which should be reassuring to the patient who has had a stroke. The services of his doctor are augmented by the equipment available for solving some of his problems and by the skilled people at hand. These can be especially important for the patient during the first few days.

His doctor will be busy, too. It is during this initial period that he must decide what tests to make, arrive at a final diagnosis, and determine on the treatment. He doesn't have too much time.

Once he has decided on the treatment he can be thankful that the method is so new that it has been in use only in the last half of this century. Prior to about a dozen years ago there had been no useful methods, techniques, or drugs to deal with a stroke in all the centuries since doctors first became aware of the need.

Actually, the patient will probably undergo several

treatments. If he has high blood pressure the doctor will want to bring it down as soon as he can; if the stroke was caused by a blod clot he will want to take all steps to prevent more clots from forming; and he will want to repair the damage already done. There is a lot to accomplish in a short period of time.

One of the great advances in modern treatment of strokes has been in surgery. The first use of modern techniques was in 1953 in an operation performed by Dr. E. Stanley Crawford and Dr. Michael E. De Bakey, both of the Baylor University College of Medicine in Texas.

Surgery can be effective when the blocked artery is in the neck or chest, which involves about 40 per cent of the strokes caused by a block. In some cases the artery can be opened and the clot removed. In others a graft, such as I have already described, is used and the blocked area by-passed. If, however, the block occurs in a vessel inside the brain, surgery is not recommended. But when surgery can be used it is valuable because normal circulation is restored at once.

One cause of a stroke from brain hemorrhage is an aneurysm, as I have already mentioned. This is brought about by a weak spot in the wall of a blood vessel, which then puffs out like a weak spot in a balloon. As it fills with blood and expands, the wall of the vessel gets thinner and eventually reaches a breaking point. When that happens, it usually begins with a small leak permitting a mere trickle of blood into the brain. This is enough, however, to bring about a stroke. Sometimes the leak will heal itself, but this does not happen often. Unless something is done quickly the leak soon becomes a full rupture. How serious this is can be seen in the fact that only about half of such patients have survived.

Here surgery has been the only answer. But that, too, has had its dangers. The operation involves sawing through the skull and lifting a piece of it, then tying off the aneurysm with a clip, or closing the artery with clips on each side. The great danger is that the aneurysm might accidentally be touched, causing it to rupture. Still, this is preferable to waiting for it to burst of its own accord.

Now something new has come along for the treatment of this condition, even while this book was being written. The idea belongs to Dr. John P. Gallagher, of Georgetown University, and Harrison P. Hagemeyer, a retired lab machinist, who built the necessary equipment at the Naval Research Laboratory in Washington.

The apparatus consists of a long, slender air gun which will shoot a hog's hair, measuring $\frac{1}{4}$ inch long and $\frac{1}{200}$ inch in diameter. The gun works on 50 pounds of air pressure.

With this new treatment, the same section is sawed in the skull and the piece lifted. The gun then fires the hog's hair into the blood-filled swelling. The introduction of a foreign body into the aneurysm causes it to clot. As it clots it also shrinks. Within a few minutes the blood in the entire blister is clotted, sealing itself off from the main path of the artery and removing the danger of the weakened wall.

Thus far it has been used in only a few operations, all successful. Before long other surgeons will be able to get the equipment and there should soon be a change in the statistics on stroke from this cause.

Surgery is also used sometimes when hemorrhage is the cause of the stroke, but there are many times when it is not feasible. In these cases it can only be hoped that the rupture will heal itself and that the released blood will be absorbed without great damage.

With blood clotting there are three possibilities. Surgery may be the answer, as I've already pointed out. In some instances, the clot will already have hardened so much that no more need be done about it, since it's done all the damage it will ever do. This was so in my case. When this happens, once the stroke is completed, the chief problems are rehabilitation and making sure that clots will not form in the future. If the clot has not hardened and an operation does not seem advisable, the clot can probably be dissolved with anticoagulant drugs. The same drugs are then used to prevent other clots.

I pointed out earlier that more government funds are spent on research for animal diseases than on all the major fatal and disabling human diseases. In a strange way one of the most dramatic advances in treating strokes came from research on animals. Several years ago an epidemic of fatal bleeding took its toll among cattle in this country. After several years of research it was discovered that rotten sweet clover produced a substance, called dicoumarin, that prevented the clotting of blood and was the cause of death among the cattle.

The cause of hemorrhagic disease in cattle was easily arrived at; the farmers stopped feeding them rotten sweet clover.

In the meantime, chemists went to work and soon learned to make the substance synthetically from coal tar and produced the first drug that prevented clotting. At first it was used to prevent clotting after an operation. Research continued and in recent years the drug has been vastly improved and has become a great lifesaver for many stroke victims.

As used now, these drugs will prevent the growth of clots already in the blood stream and will dissolve those clots which have not become too hardened. They will insure against fewer clots breaking loose which may have formed after an operation. They make it less likely that clots will form in the future—an important advance because the presence of a clot makes the patient susceptible to more.

These drugs are nearly always used in connection with drugs which will keep the blood pressure at a normal level and medication for the control of hypertension. When taken, it must be under the close supervision of a physician.

There are sometimes other facts in relationship to strokes which I have not previously mentioned. Certain heart diseases or irregularities may cause blood clots to form around the heart and these clots eventually break loose and end up causing a stroke. For example, a person may have a damaged heart from rheumatic fever during childhood. The damage is slight and the person has learned to live with it so that it does not represent a threat to his life. But there may be blood clots around the heart which will break loose twenty or thirty years later, causing a stroke.

For this reason, a stroke patient's doctor will also want to make sure about the condition of the patient's heart. If there is any irregularity, treatment may include drugs to improve the efficiency of the heart and to lower the sodium, or salt, content of the body. Too much salt causes the body to retain an overabundance of fluids, which places a heavier burden on the heart.

A rather rare disease, called polycythemia, may contribute to the cause of strokes. It is a condition which causes an increase in red blood cells to as much as two or three times the normal amount and increases the iron content as much as 50 per cent. This, then, causes sludging in the blood vessels and increases the danger of clots. Treatment often calls for one of the oldest medications known to man—bloodletting. Fortunately, the patient doesn't have to go to the barbershop or rent a leech, as did his ancestors. About a pint of blood taken every two or three months keeps down the red blood cell count and removes much of the danger. Another approach is the use of radioactive isotopes which control the production of red blood cells. In both cases, the treatment will probably be supplemented by anticoagulants.

That arteriosclerosis, high blood pressure, hypertension, and strokes are related has been known to the medical profession for many years. Considerable attention has been given especially to arteriosclerosis, since it is believed to be a basic factor in many of the diseases of age. The research in this field has produced an interesting by-path related to strokes.

It was noted that there were far fewer strokes and heart attacks, and a corresponding low incidence of arteriosclerosis, among women than men—but only during the years when the women were menstruating and capable of bearing children. Following the menopause, or change of life, women began to catch up with the men in incidence of strokes and heart disease. In this age bracket they even show a higher death rate from strokes than do men.

As I've stated elsewhere, doctors have long been interested in the level of cholesterol in the blood as related to arteriosclerosis. It is known that this level rises with age no matter how high it was in younger years. They believe that the rise is due to a change in the fats in the blood. Here they made another interesting discovery. These changes in the fat occur in men as soon as they become adults, but in women there is usually no change until menopause.

This led the doctors to believe that the hormones known as estrogens, which play an important role in menstruation and are often given to women after the menopause, had much to do with the low cholesterol level and less frequent occurrence of arteriosclerosis in women. The few experiments made in this area tend to show that if these hormones are given to men the cholesterol level drops, with less risk of future strokes.

Offhand, it sounds like a promising treatment—but

there is one small handicap. The hormones seem to make men less masculine. They develop larger breasts and seem to lose much of their sex drive. Most men feel they'd rather take their chances with strokes.

This research, however, is not a total loss. Researchers have been working for some time on developing a drug which will produce the same results without changing a bass voice to a sweet soprano. Within the past few months, two men in Texas indicated they'd found the answer but clinical experiments have been insufficient for wide use.

So far in this chapter we have been concerned with the various approaches open to the doctor, but what about the patient?

The first few days in the hospital, even if the patient is conscious all the time, will be pretty much a blur of vagueness to him if the stroke is serious. Everything in him will be concentrated on surviving and he won't be aware of much else. He'll know that he has trouble moving about and communicating, but it is doubtful if he will have a full awareness of this until after the stroke is completed and he is over the crisis.

At the same time, he will know when members of his family are there to see him and it will give him considerable comfort even if there is little communication.

The family should also be aware that at this point his brain is functioning much less than it will be a few weeks later. In addition to whatever permanent damage has been done to the brain by the stroke, he is also suffering from shock and the brain has not yet recovered enough to cope with all the new problems to be faced. Actually it is impossible at this stage to assay how much damage has been done.

Once the stroke is completed, the condition of the patient will vary according to the personality of the individual and the severity and location of the stroke. He may be able to speak no more than one or two words but understand everything said to him. He may be able to indicate his wishes by writing or he may not be able to write at all. He may be able to speak fairly well but have trouble understanding what is said to him. The kind of help which his family can provide at this point will be governed by these reactions.

Subject only to the orders of the doctor, however, the people who are close to the patient should visit him as much as they can. It will relieve his feeling of loneliness. If he can understand, read to him. Keep him informed about what is happening, not only on the personal level but in the world. Ask his advice about simple things which don't take too much thought, so that he'll feel he's still part of things.

Remember one thing. The individual who has gone through anything as shattering as a stroke feels that the world has ended for him—in a way it has—and it takes the efforts of everyone to pull him back into the main stream of life. The time to start is the minute the stroke is over.

13. Early to Rise

When the stroke is completed, the first thought that occurs is: What do we do now? There is much to be done but most of it will have to wait. A true evaluation of the brain damage cannot be made at once. The damaged part of the brain is still swollen and functioning at a much lower level. Similarly, little can be done about speech until healing has begun. This period usually takes six to eight weeks.

There is something, however, which not only can but must be done as soon as the doctor decides the patient is ready. That time will come while he is still in the hospital, shortly after the stroke is over. It is the beginning of physical therapy. The chief part of this should be done by a professional therapist if one is available. There are many sections of the country, however, where there is no professional physical therapist within a reasonable distance and the family may not be able to afford to bring one from another area. In this case, the therapy can be started by the doctor or nurse.

There are undoubtedly many doctors and nurses who have had no experience with physical therapy, especially in stroke cases. While they do know quite a bit about the human body and its care, I would suggest that they not try to use "common sense" in planning any therapy for the patient. There are available very clear, diagrammed guides to therapy for the stroke victim. (A list of these and where they can be obtained will be given elsewhere.) Later, a member of the family can become familiar with the exercises and take over when the patient is home. Every effort should be made, however, to secure the advice of a physician who is a specialist in this field.

Although some patients are left with only slight paralysis, a large percentage will be completely paralyzed on one side when the stroke is completed. The patient will not be able to sit up, turn over, or even change his position in the bed. And he will feel even more helpless than he is. At this point it is good for the family, and for the patient, to remember that nine out of ten stroke victims learn to walk again and that at least two out of every five recover enough to continue their jobs. These percentages, especially in the latter group, will probably increase in the future.

There is another important reason for beginning physical therapy as soon as possible. That is to avoid more damage to the paralyzed limbs.

We have two kinds of muscles in our arms and legs. There is one that pulls or pushes and another which is used for relaxing. These two muscles working together make the arms function smoothly under normal conditions. The pulling muscles are usually the stronger of the two. As a result, when a person has a stroke the arm and hand and the leg and foot are pulled into a curled, bent position. Unless the muscles are exercised regularly, they may become so stiff that they cannot be moved into more normal positions.

In addition to the exercises, other precautions can be taken in the hospital. If a professional therapist is obtained he will know all of these; a doctor or nurse may or may not know them.

The paralyzed leg must be kept from falling to one side when the patient is lying on his back. A large bath towel or a light blanket can be rolled up and placed on the outside of the leg and thigh so that the leg is held straight with the toes pointing up.

A pillow can be placed beneath the paralyzed arm and between it and the body, which will keep the arm from curling in to the body. Place a rolled napkin or small towel in the patient's hand so that the fingers will not be pulled in to form a fist.

If the patient wants to lie on his good side, a pillow should be placed beneath the paralyzed arm and another under the paralyzed leg so that they will be supported.

These few simple rules should be of help until a more complete guide can be obtained.

There is another important area in which the family

can help during the hospital days. Remember that the patient is a man or woman who in an incredibly brief time has been transformed from a fully functioning adult to one who is almost helpless and can't even talk about it. Physically and psychologically he has become dependent upon those around him. In addition the stroke has left him confused, unable to remember many things or to think in a rational fashion. He has shed his maturity as though it were a suit of old clothes and will be childish in many ways.

If there is any physical act which he can perform, even with difficulty, encourage him. For example, in my own case, my wife brought in my electric razor and one of the first things I was able to do for myself was to use my left hand to shave while she held the mirror. It made me feel less helpless to be able to do at least one normal thing.

The exercises needed at this stage are also simple but they have been carefully planned to keep the muscles limber and in good condition. This is why it is so important to get a professional therapist at first or, if not, the guides especially prepared for such cases. It is also important that the exercises include both sides of the body so that the unimpaired side won't start to deteriorate while the patient is in bed.

In some cases a patient may be confined to a wheel chair, or forced to use a cane, after leaving the hospital. Usually where this is necessary it shouldn't last long. Sometimes, the patient may have to continue to use a wheel chair but this will not keep him from going back to work.

Most therapists today prefer to not start the patient on these aids unless absolutely necessary, because the patient may tend to cling to them and delay his ability to walk and to acquire self-sufficiency. It is believed that the sooner the patient can rely on himself the sooner he will make greater efforts to overcome his disability.

Even though the patient may be able to do a few small things for himself, such as shaving, he may continue to be rather vague and unresponsive the first few days following the completion of the stroke. This will be due to the combination of brain shock and the struggle for survival. This will not, however, interfere with the early stages of the physical therapy.

The first improvement will usually be in the paralyzed leg. If the stroke is a bad one the use of the right arm seldom returns, but the right leg often regains feeling and can be used with varying degrees of success. Often this begins while the patient is in the hospital. When it does, the therapist usually tries to get the patient out of bed and on his feet as soon as possible. The quicker the leg is used for walking the better the chances for improvement.

The patient will be helped to sit up in bed and taught how to slip his good foot in under the ankle of the paralyzed limb and so swing both legs off the bed. His first attempts to walk will probably be made between parallel bars. He can hold on with his good hand and the other hand may be fastened to the bar so that it can slide along and still provide some small support. Another aid which may be used in the early days is a walking belt which enables the therapist to give support to the patient without actually holding him up. This can also be used later at home if necessary.

During this period the family should carefully check everything in the home to remove possible obstacles. Things which the family have taken for granted for years—a slight elevation from one room to another, stairs, and the like—may be too much for the patient. If these are described to the therapist he can work on these problems with the patient so that he'll be able to cope with them.

As the time approaches for the patient to be discharged (this will vary; in my case it was six weeks), new questions will arise. While all medical authorities agree that beginning therapy should be under the supervision of professionals, opinion differs about whether it is better for the patient to receive this in a rehabilitation hospital or at home.

The reasons advanced by both sides are valid. There is no question but that there are certain advantages in a modern rehabilitation hospital. The patient has the constant attention of a team of competent professionals in every area of his recovery: a psychology department, physical therapists, speech therapists, occupational therapists, and therapists in daily activities. There will also be a neurologist to check regularly on progress.

However, there may be two obstacles to this choice for most stroke victims. There are not many such hospitals in the United States at the present, perhaps none within reasonable distance of the patient's home. Secondly, the cost of such care is considerable and may be more than the patient and his family can afford.

Another group of medical authorities believes that the patient may often do better at home, surrounded by the love and concern of his family, than in the more impersonal atmosphere of a hospital. Actually, this will vary from patient to patient and family to family. It does put a big burden on the family of the patient, but if they love him and they work hard at understanding all the problems, they can be a big factor in his recovery. It should be borne in mind, however, that at least in the beginning professional therapy should be obtained if the family can afford it.

During the patient's stay in the hospital, following the completion of the stroke, the family should try to provide him with a television set. A portable set can be rented at reasonable rates. If possible, provide him also with a remote control so he can switch channels and turn the set off and on by himself. He will probably be able to follow what is happening on television better than anything else, even being read to. This will give him something he can do to entertain himself, without the frustrations from other activities, and hasten the day he can leave.

Throughout this chapter I have gone on the assumption that the patient will soon be walking to some degree, possibly even by the time he's discharged. This will be true of the majority, but there may be a few who will be confined to a wheel chair.

These patients, too, will get special physical therapy

to keep up muscle tone and help them recover the maximum of physical effort. They will also be taught to get around in the wheel chair, to help themselves in and out of the chair for toilet activities, and to generally be self-reliant. If one arm is completely paralyzed there are chairs that can be operated with the one good arm.

There was a time, not so long ago, when it was believed that a stroke meant the person was going to be a hopeless case for the rest of his life, confined to an institution or a back bedroom in the home. This is no longer true.

Given the proper treatment from the beginning there is no reason why the majority of stroke victims cannot build a new life for themselves—as satisfying and rewarding as the one I've already started to build for myself.

14. Going Home

The big day has arrived and the patient is going home. This will be the beginning of a long period of strain for everyone concerned, but at first the biggest burden will fall on the family. They will have to understand many new things about the patient so that they can be of the utmost assistance in his recovery. They will be called upon to exhibit more tolerance than ever before, for the patient will likely take out all of his irritability on them rather than on his doctor and therapists.

I'd like to begin this chapter with an outline of a few things that can be done at once to make the homecoming easier and get the patient started off in the best way.

The patient should have his own bed rather than sleep with another person. Use a standard level house bed, so that his feet can reach the floor, with a firm mattress instead of foam rubber. If the mattress isn't a firm one, place a piece of plywood under it. If the patient has partially recovered use of the paralyzed leg and is continuing his physical therapy it may not be necessary to continue propping up the affected leg and arm with rolled towels, but be sure to discuss this first with the therapist or doctor.

Generally, a straight-backed chair is best for sitting, although in my case I found an adjustable contour chair extremely restful.

If there's a shower in the home this will probably be easier for the patient than using the tub. Put a stool or a straight-backed chair in the shower so that he can take it sitting down. He may have to be helped into it at first, but if so he should be encouraged to do it alone as soon as possible. In the event that there is no shower, wall rails can be placed around a tub to make it easier for the patient to get in and out; sometimes a seat in the tub may help. These are all available.

Clothing is another problem. Most patients will have trouble with zippers and these should be replaced by buttons or snaps. There is also a new material, called Velcro, which is nylon with loops on one side and hooks on the other, which can be fastened by exerting a slight pressure. This is sold in strips and can be sewn to any garment.

When the patient is a woman, care should be taken to see that her dresses do not fasten in the back. If the opening is in front, or on the side that she can reach with her good hand, she will soon be able to dress and undress herself. A little tailoring can also change the fasteners on a brassière from the back to the side so that she can manage it.

The cuff button on a man's shirt can be changed on the side of his good arm, enlarging the space so that it can be slipped on while buttoned. If he prefers cuff links, he can use the method described in an earlier chapter.

In the beginning the patient can wear shoes without laces. They are easy to get, especially in the "loafer" type of shoe. Later the patient can try the method of tying I use, illustrated in the latter part of the book. A shoe horn with a long handle makes it easier to put them on.

Elastic should be put in the pajama pants, as my wife did for me, and the patient will have no trouble with them.

Bow ties that clip on can be used until the patient feels up to attempting the knotting of a regular tie.

If a man has trouble fastening and unfastening a belt, get elastic suspenders, which should solve the problem.

Remember that when the patient comes home he may be very childish in his reactions to everything. The family must realize that this is to be expected during the early stages and learn how to cope with it while helping him to work toward a more mature attitude. There will probably be a tendency on the part of the family to be overprotective and this must be avoided. Have a sympathetic approach to his problems but don't express too much sympathy. This will only increase his self-pity and delay his recovery. Try to emphasize his accomplishments rather than his symptoms and failures.

In every way possible the patient should be kept progressing and trying new things, but be careful not to push him into efforts which are beyond his ability. It will only discourage him. Nearly all stroke victims experience depression but this occurs usually less often in the late afternoon than at other times. Then is the best time to urge him to try new things. Any new thing, no matter how simple, that he can do will also help to lessen depression.

With the stubborn patient—and many of them are stubborn—it is a good idea to be permissive to a certain degree and try to get him to accept suggestions when he is in a better frame of mind. If the doctor has prescribed a diet which disturbs the patient, don't be too rigid about it. Discuss it with the doctor, who may agree to vary it a little for the time being, then work back to it gradually.

Since many patients have difficulty in focusing their attention on a thing for more than a few minutes, and some of them have difficulty in understanding what is being said to them, members of the family find that they unconsciously raise their voices as though this would overcome the lack of understanding. Try to avoid this. More will be achieved by speaking slowly and softly, using short sentences.

It is well to remember that the person who has been disabled by a stroke, or only partially disabled, may tend to use his disability as a way of controlling the rest of the family. He may expect them to run at the slightest sound from him and to do everything for him that he desires. At the time, this will seem perfectly logical to him. After all, he tells himself, he is sick and crippled while they are perfectly healthy. The family tends to respond the way he wants them to. This is a mistake, for the patient

157

may never make an effort to do things for himself as long as somebody obeys his every whim.

Despite the great variety of reactions in stroke victims, doctors agree that there are traits common to almost everyone who has had a stroke. They are:

Mental confusion

Depression

Inability to think in abstract terms

Anxiety and tension

Apprehension

Compulsiveness

Indifference

Rigid attitude toward new tasks

Stereotyped behavior

Irritability

Apathy and withdrawal from active participation in life

Impatience and stubbornness

Tendency to emphasize and exaggerate his illness

Disturbance of the body image

If you study this list carefully you will see that most of these reactions are psychological, or emotional, rather than physical. I have mentioned the importance of emotional problems among the causes of stroke, but there should be an understanding of their role in recovering from a stroke. If the family understands this it will help them in their efforts to aid the patient; later, when the patient is able to comprehend abstract ideas, it will be valuable to him in his efforts to help himself.

Just as the last few years have seen tremendous strides

in the treatment of strokes, the same period has witnessed a heartening progress in rehabilitation. One of the biggest steps has been to view the patient as a total being; in other words, the idea is not to limit rehabilitation to the exercise of one set of muscles or merely to give the patient a new vocabulary, but to realize that every part of the patient's existence has been affected by the stroke and must be involved in the treatment. The pioneer in this concept was the Institute of Physical Medicine and Rehabilitation of New York University, headed by Dr. Howard A. Rusk.

This approach to rehabilitation actually began in 1948 when an investigation was started to determine what value, if any, there would be in adding a psychiatrist, a psychiatric social worker, and a psychologist to the existing teams of physicians, orthopedists, therapists of all kinds, and other professional workers in the field of rehabilitation. The following years have proved that such a combination can do a much better job of restoring the disabled person to society. And this is why many doctors today do recommend that some part of rehabilitation be spent in such a hospital wherever it is possible.

Among the earliest emotional symptoms after a stroke is depression. It varies in intensity from individual to individual, depending on the personality of the victim. There may be a simple depressed mood, frequent crying; a lack of interest in the surroundings; or it may go as far as attempts at suicide. A patient may just lie in bed insisting that he cannot do the exercises, or he may take the attitude that nothing is going to help.

How long the depression lasts depends largely on the patient himself. Following a stroke, some time goes by before he faces the reality of his situation. He is depressed but he believes that his disability is only temporary and that he will soon be completely cured. If this refusal to recognize what has happened to him continues overlong, the depression will probably deepen and become more firmly a part of his personality. He may refuse to do anything to rehabilitate himself, insisting that it is useless since he will soon be cured. This condition may last several years. Even if he does get over this stage, so much time has been lost that it will be difficult for him to rebuild muscles and recover speech.

I think that, in my own case, I had considerable depression up until the day I took a good honest look and recognized that I would have to bear with a certain amount of disability the rest of my life. That was a very rough time, but after I accepted it and determined that I would try my best to overcome it, I had few periods of depression and these did not last long.

During this latter period there is sometimes another reaction, although I do not believe that I experienced it. The patient may alternate between blaming himself for what happened and blaming the outside world. In the first instance he will fall back into his depression. In the second, he will react by being aggressive about everything he wants and by showing hostility toward those around him. This may be an especially difficult stage for the family when it occurs.

A certain amount of depression is "normal" for the

situation in the early days, but if it gets out of proportion or lasts unduly, the cause probably goes back to something long before the stroke.

Anxiety, or fear, is another symptom which may continue much longer than depression. Part of this may be realistic and "normal" for the patient's condition. Examples of this might be a fear of falling when first learning to use the disabled leg, or the fear of injuring the paralyzed hand and not noticing it until a serious loss of blood has occurred, the paralysis having caused a loss of sensations. But these are dangers which the patient can deal with and overcome. I've already related that I had a few falls in the beginning, but it is a long time since I've had one and I doubt if there will be any more. I've had only one slight accident to my right hand and I noticed that at once.

Other anxieties are felt which are not so realistic and can interfere with the patient's progress. So many of these exist, again depending on the individual's personality, that I will not try to give them all. Probably the most frequent are the fear of being looked at or of being so unattractive that he will be socially unacceptable.

Sometimes a patient may feel that his stroke is a punishment for something he did in the past. Such a patient will often refuse to go outdoors because people seeing him will know of his guilt.

While the family's treatment of the patient may be of help in such situations, it is wise to consult a psychiatrist if the patient is not in a rehabilitation hospital.

Since we are on the problem of anxieties, I would like

to mention another problem not often discussed in books on strokes and which the patient may not even speak of to his family doctor. That is the sexual life of the patient. Occasionally his physical condition may diminish his sexual drive or cause a lack of sexual interest or response. It is more apt to be a psychological problem, again involving anxiety. A man becomes aware, as he begins to recover, that his disability interferes to some degree with the traditional sexual aggressiveness of the male. His disability has in itself made him feel less of a man, and this feeling is soon transferred to his thoughts about sex. The fear of impotence may grow until he will have great difficulty performing the sexual act when he finally attempts it, which convinces him that his fear was justified.

Another problem which faces the male stroke victim is when his paralysis makes it difficult to change position while resting in bed, so what would be the "normal" position to assume in a sexual relationship may be impossible or, at best, awkward. This exaggerates his feeling that he has lost his manhood.

Unless the man's wife completely understands the problem and is able to adapt to it they may be coping with a difficulty they cannot solve alone. The wife must become the dominant one in their sexual life, assuming the aggressive role which has always belonged to her husband, and she must be able to do it in a manner which will not increase her husband's anxiety. If she can manage this there is no reason why they can't enjoy a full sex life as they did before.

The case of a woman who has had a stroke is somewhat different but she, too, has her sexual anxieties and they may be just as harmful. While she may feel impotent because of her disability, the physical manifestations are not the same as in the male. If she has not had her menopause she will be much concerned over her possible inability to have children and this will cause anxiety.

The disabled woman is also very much concerned with her feminine role in life. She begins to feel that she has nothing to offer and that nobody will want her.

Her problems are much more direct ones, not complicated by a need to be aggressive, so that if her husband continues to show by kindness and love that he does want her she should soon start to recover from any such anxieties.

Of course, some individuals are disinterested in sex or have found no fulfillment in it before the stroke and use the disability as an excuse to avoid what they had merely tolerated before. There are probably some married couples who have grown away from each other and they will both use the disability of one partner as a reason for refraining from any future sex relationship.

Whatever form it takes, sexual anxieties interfere with the rehabilitation of the patient and the problems should be resolved as soon as possible. If the husband and wife cannot do it themselves they should seek outside help, through their physician or a psychiatrist.

At times individual fears are developed, not common to most patients. It is usually safe to assume that these often are related to an incident in the patient's life prior to the stroke. Examples might be a fear of physical therapy because the manipulation of the limbs arouses sexual thoughts, or a fear of crossing streets because of the necessity of stepping up from the street to the curb. Such fears nearly always must be dealt with professionally.

Another symptom often exhibited by the patient is one of dependency. This is certainly a throwback to a pre-stroke age, because as infants and children we are all dependent on others. The need to lean on others usually disappears as we mature. The person who has a stroke is, in a way, thrown back to that early age, for at first he is unable to do anything for himself and is usually unable to express himself any better than a very young child. Even when he gets out of the hospital he is forced to be dependent on others to some degree.

It is possible that an unconscious memory is revived of how pleasant it was to have every want supplied. Consciously he will be eager to get well and equally determined unconsciously to remain ill. Such a patient may become a tyrant, using his disability to order the family around, or he may be more subtle and seem to reject most help while he develops little tricks that will get the family to obey his whims voluntarily. It is impossible to tell him bluntly what he is doing, so the family must work patiently to change his attitude. If this doesn't work within a reasonable time, they should resort to professional help.

Earlier, I mentioned that a stroke causes a disturbance of the body image. All of us, starting early in childhood, have an idea of what we look like and how we use our bodies. This idea may not be necessarily accurate, and others may see us quite differently, but unless the individual is mentally disturbed it will be based on some degree of truth. (A person may have a potential of beauty and grace and not have developed it, although he thinks he has.) So when he suffers a permanent physical disability he is faced with the need to revise his picture of himself.

Some patients flatly refuse to do this for a long period of time. Sometimes this takes the form of not understanding what has happened to them. They insist that they do not know of any reason why they should have trouble walking or be unable to use one arm. This reaction occurs equally to educated persons (even those with medical experience) and the uneducated. They accept no explanation, and they will go from doctor to doctor asking why this has happened to them.

The denial of the disability takes other forms in some patients. As soon as the stroke has been completed and the patient becomes more aware of what is happening, he will decide that a paralyzed arm belongs to someone else and demand that it be removed from his bed. Often the patient will think the arm belongs to a dead husband or wife. One patient, whose paralyzed arm was lying on her chest, believed that it belonged to her dead husband who had returned and was caressing her.

Others insist that the paralyzed limb is a separate entity with a life of its own. This concept is helped by the fact that the fingers of a paralyzed hand will often move by reflex action. The patient sees this, but doesn't feel anything, which helps to convince him. Such patients often personify the disabled part by giving it a man's or woman's name. Others have been known to name the arm or leg after a distant country or continent.

Because the patient insists that he is not disabled, he will often refuse therapy or any sort of physical aid since he "doesn't need it."

This is a situation which, if it continues, cannot be handled by the family alone and they will need professional help. There are enough real obstacles for the disabled person in our society to engage all of his strength and ability; when unreal ones are added to these he's in for trouble unless he can get over them.

Most of the things previously mentioned in this chapter will not be day-to-day problems for the family if the patient has gone into a rehabilitation hospital for the basic steps in his recovery. I am going to assume, however, that this is presently impossible for the majority, due to the scarcity and location of hospitals or to the cost. I am also assuming that I speak to a family that doesn't want to send the patient to a nursing home or state institution and forget about him. Unfortunately, this has happened to too many stroke victims, resulting not only in a tragedy for them but in a loss of many useful citizens. It is estimated that about 1,250,000 stroke patients are now in some kind of institution where they get, at best, minimal rehabilitation. It is also estimated that 25 per cent of the persons in many state mental hospitals are stroke patients. Although they have suffered brain damage, I seriously doubt they belong with the mentally disturbed and insane.

However, if the family decides that the patient is going to be at home, their "education" in understanding his problems and the ways in which they can help will continue for years. But they should be able to grasp most of the basic things by the time he is released from the hospital and be capable of valuable assistance in getting him well started on the road to recovery. Such preparation and information will also make it much easier for themselves.

The healing process in the brain usually takes from six to twelve weeks. It may be completed, as in my case, when the patient arrives home, or it may take a few weeks longer. Until such time the concentration will be mostly on physical therapy, but once the brain has healed it is time to move ahead in all areas.

The first thing is to learn exactly how much damage has been done. The family should make every effort to see that the patient is tested by a psychologist, who can determine the extent of the brain damage and the potential of the patient, and by professionals in the fields of speech, daily living activities, and occupational therapy. Also, the patient should also be examined by a neurologist. These tests are so important that I would urge that the family arrange for them even if it requires a trip of some distance. The cost will not be too much and the results are invaluable.

With the tests over, speech therapy should be started promptly. It is much easier to establish new patterns in speech than to overcome the faults which develop when there is no therapy for several months. If the family does not live in a large city there may still be a speech therapist near enough to call in. Information as to where to find a list of such therapists will be included later. If a professional is not available and the family has to work on the patient's speech themselves, there are certain methods and guides available and complete information will also be given for these.

Once the family knows the range of the patient's abilities they can probably handle the activities of daily living therapy providing they familiarize themselves with the methods and aids. I have included enough of these for a beginning; others are easily available.

In the meantime the patient will be on constant medication. If he has high blood pressure there will be a prescription for that, and possible tranquilizers for his hypertension. If his stroke was caused by a blood clot he will be on anticoagulants. Make sure that he takes the proper amount of medication each day.

This should be done without constant nagging or an attitude that emphasizes the patient's disabilities. Since he may have trouble remembering whether he has taken a drug or not, it's a good idea to give him a small container and to place in it each morning the drugs he should take during the day. This can be done until his memory has improved to the point where it is no longer necessary.

Remember that the worst should now be over, and everyone can concentrate on improving the patient's condition. The work won't be easy but the rewards are worth it.

15. What Is Happening?

After the patient has been brought home and everyone is trying to settle into a routine, new problems and new questions will arise almost daily. This may not be so in the beginning, if the family has prepared for what is to be expected, for the patient will usually not have too much drive toward rehabilitation during that period. The time when the family needs still more information will come after the brain injury has healed and the patient has passed the crisis of realizing that no miracle will suddenly restore his health.

Until then, however, the biggest worry will be to see that the patient keeps up with his physical therapy and to cope with his depression, anxiety, and irritability. It's probably a good thing that it's limited to that, for the family, as well as the patient, will need a period of adjustment before they tackle the big job ahead.

I believe, as do many doctors, that even if the patient is able to obtain complete professional therapy it is important for the family to know as much as they can about what is going on. As soon as the patient can understand, he should be equally informed. If for any reason the patient is unable to have professional help, the need for information is all the more vital. A book such as this can only provide an over-all basic understanding, a few beginning guides to the early stages of rehabilitation, and sources of further details concerning what happens and what must be done.

Fortunately there is considerable literature on the subject, and a great many self-help aids to rehabilitation; these are being added to almost daily.

Let's start at the beginning. I have covered very briefly the need for support of paralyzed limbs while the patient is in bed, the necessity for proper exercises, and the requirements of the first few days out of bed. For more complete information, with clear illustrations, the U.S. Government Printing Office has provided a very good pamphlet called *Strike Back at Stroke*. It can be secured by sending 40 cents to the Superintendent of Documents, U.S. Government Printing Office, Washington 25, D.C. There is also a very good short pamphlet, *Early Management of a Patient with a Stroke* by Donald Covalt, M.D., reprinted from *Medical Times* for April, 1958; this can be obtained from the Institute of Physical Medicine and Rehabilitation, New York University–Bellevue Medical Center, 400 East 34th Street, New York 16, N.Y.

If the stroke victim is female her normal job may be as the homemaker. In these days of the career woman we often lose sight of the fact that she is as important to the home as the one who brings in the money. When the wife and mother has become disabled, not only is the family life disrupted by her disability but it may add an extra, even insuperable hardship if someone is hired to take over the housekeeping.

The problem of trying to help her regain her function in this field is one which sometimes applies to men. Often when a man has been so crippled by a stroke that he cannot go back into gainful employment he will decide to take over the housework while his wife goes out to earn the money. This not only solves the money problem but also enables the man to feel that he can still make a contribution to his family and so will help in his over-all rehabilitation.

At first glance, the patient may think that it's completely impossible for her to do the cooking, cleaning, and so on. She may be in a wheel chair or, if not, still has trouble in getting around. Also, she probably can use only one hand. It can be done, however. There will be the need for some readjustment, not only on the part of everyone concerned but in the setup of the kitchen.

Many products are now manufactured which make functioning easier for the handicapped in the kitchen and elsewhere. In addition, therapy specialists have worked out hundreds of methods which enable the stroke patient to do things which seem difficult.

For example, the patient may think that peeling potatoes with one hand is impossible, whereas it is actually easy. Pin the potato to a cutting board by putting a stainless steel knitting needle, or something similar, through it, and then one hand can be used to wield a peeler. Washing dishes is not too difficult but something like an encrusted pot represents a problem. A double suction cup can be put between the pot and the table to hold the utensil in place while it is scoured.

These are only two of the many ways in which the homemaker can be helped. The Institute of Physical Medicine and Rehabilitation has a model kitchen for the handicapped. If the patient lives in the New York City area she might find it valuable to go there for training therapy. If not, they have put out a valuable booklet, with many pictures, called *A Manual for Training the Disabled Homemaker* (Rehabilitation Monograph VIII), which can be obtained from the Institute of Physical Medicine and Rehabilitation, New York University– Bellevue Medical Center, 400 East 34th Street, New York 16, N.Y. Also available at the same address is a more general pamphlet, *Self-Help Devices for Rehabilitation.*

A company in New York City specializes in the manufacture of self-help devices and puts out a catalogue of their products. This is the Fascole Corporation, 257 Park Avenue South, New York 10, N.Y.

When a stroke has affected the patient's language ability the doctors call it aphasia. The word actually means loss of language, but it refers to an impairment in speech, reading, writing, spelling, mathematics, understanding what others are saying, telling time, and even the recognition of objects. The patient may or may not have all of these symptoms but will nearly always have some at first. Shortly after the critical period of the stroke he may improve somewhat, but as I have emphasized he will need speech therapy to communicate adequately.

If the patient lives in one of the major cities of the United States he will have little trouble in locating a speech therapist. In other parts of the country it may be more difficult. Even his doctor, or the local hospital, may not know where the nearest therapist can be found. There is, however, a directory of qualified speech therapists in America which can be obtained from the American Speech and Hearing Associates, 1001 Connecticut Avenue, N.W., Washington 6, D.C.

If no speech therapist is located within easy distance, or if the cost is too high, as a last resort the family should undertake the task themselves. This should be done as soon as possible after the brain has healed.

I will have more to say about this later, with information that will help bridge any interval before you get the aids that are available.

When my wife was helping me with speech and writing we used two sets of cards made by the Milton Bradley Company of Springfield, Massachusetts. One is called *Understanding Numbers;* the other, *Picture Words for Beginners.* These are commonly used for very young children but I think they were quite helpful in getting me started on therapy. Both sets use a combination of pictures and words or numbers and are intended to improve reading and speaking and the ability to do simple mathematics.

A more specialized aid to therapy is the *Aphasia Rehabilitation Manual and Therapy Kit*, by Martha L. Taylor and Morton Marks, M.D. It can be obtained from Saxon Press, 207 East 37th Street, New York 16, N.Y., for $7.50. Both authors are connected with the Institute of Physical Medicine and Rehabilitation, from which you can obtain a helpful pamphlet, *Understanding Aphasia*, by Martha L. Taylor.

If the patient lives in a community where a number of persons are interested in this subject, there are films available which can provide needed information. The following is a list of film titles and where they can be obtained.

Step by Step in Everyday Tasks. Slide film No. 643, U.S.D.A. Extension Service, Washington 25, D.C.

Now She Does It. Household Finance Corporation, 919 North Michigan Ave., Chicago 2, Illinois.

Within Your Reach. Film Service, New York State College of Agriculture, Ithaca, N.Y.

A number of organizations have published pamphlets and booklets with valuable information. There is also *The Crippled Child Magazine*, which may contain many hints for adults as well as children. It is published bimonthly and a subscription can be obtained from The National Society for Crippled Children and Adults, 2023 West Ogden Avenue, Chicago 12, Illinois, for $3 per year.

Following is a list of other publications and where they can be obtained.

The Disabled in a Modern World. The proceedings of the Fifth World Congress of the International Society for the Welfare of Cripples, 127 East 52nd Street, New York,

N.Y. It is also possible that where answers cannot be found to specific problems this organization might be able to help.

Easier Homemaking. No. 529. Agricultural Experiment Station, Purdue University, Lafayette, Indiana.

Easy Does It. This is a series of leaflets with valuable information for the disabled. It is put out by the Department of Home Economics, Wayne University, Detroit, Michigan.

The Kitchen Reporter, published by Kelvinator Kitchen, Detroit, Michigan, includes many fine articles on the handicapped homemaker's problems and how they can be solved. Write and ask them what they have available.

Old Versus New Ironing Methods, by Margaret Coleman, Teachers College, Columbia University. This may be obtained by writing to Information Center, Proctor Electric Company, 480 Lexington Avenue, New York 17, N.Y.

Pots and Pans for Your Kitchen. House and Garden Bulletin No. 2 by Elizabeth Beveridge. Superintendent of Documents, U.S. Government Printing Office, Washington 25, D.C.

Put It on Wheels, by Rupert Perry. University of Kentucky Agricultural Experiment Station, Lexington 29, Kentucky.

A Guide for the Kitchen Planner, by Maude Wilson. No. 482. Oregon State College, Corvallis, Oregon.

Kitchen Utility Wagon and Lap Table, by Mabel C. Mack, No. 482. Oregon State College, Corvallis, Oregon.

Convenience in Kitchen Cupboards, by Jean Warren.

No. C-192. University of California Publication Office, Giannini Hall, Berkeley 4, California.

Home Safety for the Physically Limited. National Electric Products Corporation, Pittsburgh, Pennsylvania.

Additional readings will be suggested in a later chapter. There is enough material on almost every aspect of the stroke victim so there is no reason why the family and the patient cannot be fully informed on the ways that he can function and continue to make progress.

16. In the Beginning Was the Word

Not every stroke patient has aphasia, or language impairment, but it is safe to say that many patients have. Generally speaking, those who get no speech therapy are condemned to go through the rest of their lives with very little or no communication with their fellow men. There may be a slight improvement over the condition at the time the stroke is completed but it will not go beyond that without help and training. Since writing and spelling are also affected, they cannot depend on that method of communicating.

Incidentally, not only stroke causes aphasia. It may come from brain injury due to a fall or a blow on the head. The age or intelligence of the person has nothing to do with it.

One area in which the formal education of the patient may have some bearing is in speech rehabilitation. The person with little education may make a more satisfactory recovery but this is because his goal will be nearer and he more quickly approaches the vocabulary and speech that was his before the brain damage. The person with more education—the professional, for example— may never be able to achieve the standards he demands of himself. The result will be constant frustration and irritation, interfering with every phase of his rehabilitation.

There is one warning which should be given to the families of those who have language difficulties. Often the patient will be able to swear, or use obscene language, fluently. Or he may be able to sing certain songs with no trouble at all. This may encourage the family to believe that he is well on his way to normal speech, but it is not so. The same thing may apply to stereotyped phrases such as "A rolling stone gathers no moss." All of these are automatic speech, being non-intellectual and having no value in social communication. Sometimes, however, words from automatic speech can be used in the effort to restore useful speech.

Again, since anyone will benefit more from professional speech therapy, this chapter is written primarily for those who have no access to such professional help. But it also helps in cases where the patient has outside help, in aiding the family to understand the problems so that they can give more assistance to the patient during and following therapy.

A patient who finds it almost impossible to speak will often be able to read and write with no difficulty. This should have no bearing on the question of speech therapy. While it is true that he will be able to write out the things he wishes to communicate, he should still be encouraged to regain as much of his speech as possible. The voice is psychologically important to all of us and there will be considerable frustration in not being able to use it intelligibly, no matter how well the patient can write. Praise the patient when he attempts to speak; show pleasure at his progress, no matter how slow. It is fine to correct the mistakes he may make, providing it isn't done in a nagging manner, which is more apt to discourage him. When he realizes that he can recover this ability, he will push himself as fast as he can manage.

Many people tend to be uncomfortable in the presence of someone having speech difficulty. Or they may show impatience when a sentence is unduly long in coming out. If members of the family have these reactions they should do their best to keep them hidden. Expressing them may cause the patient to withdraw and cease trying.

If the patient is to be given therapy at home it is wise to remember that he will not be able to concentrate long at first. Keep the sessions short but have them once or twice a day. Long periods will tire him and the resulting mental confusion may be discouraging.

I have said earlier that one of the big advances in rehabilitation has been the awareness that the stroke patient must be treated as a whole person. It is one of the most important things to remember. This means that it is not enough to give him speech therapy or physical therapy and ignore all of the other things that have happened to him.

Perhaps the family's biggest contribution, whether therapy is outside or in the home, is that of creating a warm atmosphere in which the patient feels himself to be a participant. Don't merely give him attention at therapy time and mealtime and then isolate him in his own room the rest of the time. Be with him as much as possible. If there are little helpful things he can do, encourage him. Within the range of his understanding discuss family problems and other things with him and show that his opinion is important. Even if he can't speak much he will be able to nod and shake his head, or in other ways indicate his reactions.

As soon as he is able to get out of the house make a point of going to the movies occasionally. When he can walk, take strolls together. They may be short at first but they can be of longer duration later. While walking, talk to him about the sights; this may also help him in the recovery of his speech.

When I first began to walk outdoors, my wife and I often went together. She would slip her arm through my disabled right arm—a normal gesture when we went walking before my stroke; it made me feel less conspicuous and gave me a sense of security even though she was not actually exerting physical support.

Try in other ways to make his life as nearly as possible what it was before. If he liked a drink or two before the evening meal, continue the custom—provided his doctor agrees. If he enjoyed an occasional card game, see that it's arranged. Even the patient who has trouble with numbers will usually be able to play cards with no difficulty.

It will be found that these activities contribute to the progress he makes in speaking and walking. The patient's progress, or lack of it, is closely related to other factors such as depression, emotional problems, or fatigue.

Remember that nearly everything in this book is aimed at the average stroke victim, in so far as possible. There are a few patients whose speech will be only mildly affected and who may not even need therapy. The impairment will range from mild to such severity wherein patients cannot speak, read, write, or understand. Their condition may not be as bad as it seems at first but they certainly cannot be treated at home. The family must then find some way of obtaining professional help.

Before going on, I would like to correct another fallacy. Many persons mistake the speech difficulties and the mental confusion that follows a stroke with senility or mental illness. As a matter of record, a high percentage of patients in state mental hospitals have been placed there after a stroke. This is not only a mistake; it is harmful. The stroke victim does have a certain amount of brain damage but in most cases he will be just as intelligent and as sane as before. Treating him like a mental patient would mean to rob him of his chance to recover and once again be a useful member of society.

In the interval following the stroke, the patient may seem to be quite different in his behavior. He will get tired more easily, show less interest in the things that once attracted him, and become irritated or upset by small, everyday events. The family may feel that his whole personality has been altered by the stroke. This is not so. Some of these changes, such as the tendency to become irritated, may have always been a part of him, but in the past he was able to control them better. All these reactions, however, will begin to disappear as he makes progress in his rehabilitation.

Some people, especially patients, believe that their language problems can be treated by medicine or by physical treatment of the throat. It can't be done. The patient will probably be on medication to relieve his physical and emotional condition and this may make it easier for him to work on his speaking problems, but there will be no direct effect. The only answer to that is hard work to rebuild speech patterns and to deal with written and spoken concepts.

Although speech therapy starts with methods that are used with very young children, it does not help to begin him on consonant and vowel sounds. There are few patients who can't manage these, so it is a waste of time. Start him on words, but don't worry about sentences until he seems ready for them. At first, the important thing is to teach him nouns, chiefly those that apply to his immediate needs. Words like "book," "television," "bathroom," "bread," and "shirt" are specifically related to the things that concern him most; ability to pronounce them will establish immediate communication. Verbs, adverbs, and so on, as well as abstract words, can come much later when the patient is able to cope with them. Teaching him these too soon will only result in confusion.

It has often been suggested that the patient be taught sign language or encouraged to write down all his wants. I am inclined to believe this is a mistake. It may be even more difficult to teach him a sign language; but even if it succeeds it is apt to keep him from learning to speak again. It won't serve him outside of the home—certainly not on any job.

How long should speech therapy last? There is no way to answer this in general terms. It will depend on the extent of brain damage and on the personality of the patient. In any event, the period in which the patient needs help, whether from the family or the therapist, will certainly range from several months to several years. It is my belief that once the need for help is past, self-therapy takes over and probably continues as long as the patient lives. I know that I am continually learning to speak and understand words that were impossible for me only a few months ago.

Speech therapy does not consist only of relearning how to say words but should include other uses of language. Being able to write often helps with speaking. In most cases of speech difficulties it is the right side of the body that has been impaired by the stroke, and the patient must learn to write with his left hand. He can always switch back to the right hand if it does recover; in the meantime it will increase his ability to write.

Reading is also important and should be emphasized

in the therapy session. The patient can write sentences which he reads. It is also well to have him read a paragraph and then answer questions as to the content. It will be found at first that the patient is able to concentrate for only short periods of time. He may not be able to read more than one page before he must stop, but this will improve as therapy continues.

It has often been observed that a person who speaks more than one language recovers his native language first after a stroke. This is not always true; it was English that first came back to me, not Russian. There is, however, an interesting thing about it. Russian words are spelled phonetically. If you hear a word spoken you automatically know how it is spelled. This is not true of English. So while it was English that first returned to me, I still occasionally spell a word as it sounds rather than correctly.

If the family does decide to give the patient his speech therapy at home they must realize fully how big a job it is. Don't start any sort of therapy without being sure that it is one of the recommended aids you've obtained. Irritation or impatience at the patient's slowness must never be shown, and he must not be pushed faster than he can go. Never remind him how good his speech was before the stroke. He must constantly be encouraged and never made to feel that he's a burden. It will put a big strain on the family and they must be prepared to meet it.

Remember also that professional therapy is best. The family should exhaust every avenue to such help before taking it over themselves.

If you cannot reach one of the rehabilitation centers or find a nearby therapist, one other possibility is available. Every state maintains a rehabilitation service. A person is eligible for treatment if he has a disability which is a handicap to employment, if he is of working age and if he has a reasonable chance of employment after he recovers. The services are free for those unable to pay.

If neither the family nor the physician knows the location of a rehabilitation center, information can be obtained by writing to the National Society for Crippled Children and Adults, Inc., 2023 West Ogden Avenue, Chicago 12, Illinois.

Do it as soon as possible after the stroke. A patient who does not have the chance to recover is a person lost to himself, to his family, and to society as a whole.

17. The Long Journey

When the patient has begun to make some progress in all areas of recovery, and he and his family have accepted the fact that this will not be a quick miracle but something that will take time and hard work, they can start thinking of long-term rehabilitation. But they should not fix absolute goals. Realize merely that it will take many months, perhaps several years, and determine to do the best you can.

As soon as the patient is capable of reading and understanding, the family should give him access to the information they have already obtained about strokes. The more he understands the better his chances, for he will recognize it when he is making "normal" progress and not suffer the disappointments and setbacks of waiting for a miracle.

If the stroke has been serious, involving severe impairments, the patient shouldn't be impatient to go back to work. This may cause hardships for the family but even these are preferable to having him attempt to work too soon and consequently fail.

In addition to whatever formal therapy he has, the patient should be encouraged to try for recovery in every phase of activity. If he can walk he should go out every day, by himself as much as possible. Each walk should be a little longer than the one before, although he should never overtax his strength. If his walking is slightly unsteady, he should avoid going out when the streets are wet or covered with snow, but otherwise nothing should keep him indoors—even in a wheel chair. When there are problems such as stairs to and from home, the family might find a place to live where there is direct access to the street. His ability to come and go without help, or with a minimum of help, will contribute greatly to his recovery.

Other forms of exercise should be encouraged. One of the best is swimming. Almost every disabled person can swim, even those normally confined to a wheel chair. If there is a YMCA or other organization nearby with an indoor swimming pool, the family can get the patient a membership card so that he can continue swimming in all seasons. This form of recreation is not only good for building the muscle tone and strengthening the disabled limbs; it gives him an additional social activity, one in which his disability will be less noticeable to himself and others. If the patient didn't swim before his stroke, he can learn from a competent instructor.

As I mentioned earlier, the paralyzed leg usually recovers sooner and to a greater degree than the paralyzed arm. It often regains almost all sensation while the arm has none. The patient's therapist, or the member of the family who is following an approved schedule of therapy, will work on exercises for the arm, but the patient should not be satisfied with this. He should move the arm as much as possible. While walking he can be sure that he keeps swinging the arm in rhythm to his steps. Several times a day he can take a few minutes to do his own exercises, lifting the arm as high as he can, lifting it away from his body to the side and in front, lifting it up to press the hand against his chest, and so on.

These are exercises which I did and still do daily. I'm certain that they are largely responsible for the fact that I have considerable mobility in my right arm, although it is still paralyzed. I can not only move it a great deal but can use it to carry many objects by holding them against my chest and generally get some minimal use of it in most of my activities.

The patient must remember that the more he does for himself the more he will accomplish. The only limit is his own energy and what he is capable of doing at the moment. He must also remember that his progress will be made in small steps, not in great strides, and never push himself too far or too fast. When any activity begins to tire him, he should rest awhile then try again.

The patient may be able to do a number of things around the house within a few months. No matter how small, they can be important. They will make him feel that he is contributing to the welfare of the family, thus lightening the burden for the family in the difficult task ahead. They, too, are part of his rehabilitation, no matter how trivial they may seem to him at the time.

If some thought is given to it, the family can find a number of former activities which the patient can soon attempt. Did he enjoy cards? Then arrange frequent card games, either with the family or with friends. A rack for holding cards can be bought or easily devised, so that there will be no problem in trying to play with one hand. Although the patient may have trouble with abstract numbers, he can still play a good game of cards. In my own case, I have no trouble recognizing the cards I hold, though the general use of numbers is still difficult.

There are many other games that the patient may be able to play, such as dominoes or Monopoly. Scrabble is not impossible, though many stroke victims may find they cannot play it with ease.

I've already mentioned that movies, television and radio are good ways for the patient to be relaxed and entertained and they may even be of considerable help in speech therapy. If the patient is young enough and athletically inclined, there is no reason why he can't find a way of enjoying active play. Even those in wheel chairs can participate with other handicapped people in such games as basketball and ping pong. There is even a special Olympic Games for the physically disabled.

The most difficult part of rehabilitation is to gain the awareness that a stroke is not the end of life. Once this is realized, the patient and his family can plan a program (without too definite goals) to include basic therapies, such as physical and speech, and the beginning of a new social and recreational life. This accomplished, the first breakthrough has been made. The rest is mostly hard work and patience.

18. The Crystal Ball

As rehabilitation progresses, one question becomes paramount in the minds of the patient and his family. What will his future be? Will he be able to go back to work? How far can he go toward living a "normal" life? All important questions—and the answers have tremendous meaning for those concerned.

Although there will be almost as many kinds of recovery as there are patients, the chances are good. When the brain has healed and the patient has been tested, a fairly accurate estimate can be made of the extent of damage and the probability of recovery. The doctors, however, can only tell you what is possible; they cannot predict. That depends largely on the patient and to some degree on his family.

Remember the figures I gave earlier? Nine out of every ten stroke victims are able to walk again; two out of every five are able to return to gainful employment. These are the latest figures available, but they are at least two years old. The odds may be even better now. Most of the progress in treatment and in rehabilitation has come in the past ten years and is rapidly increasing.

Only recently the victim of a stroke could almost be expected to suffer one or more additional strokes—eventually one would be fatal. Except in rare cases, today there is no reason why a second stroke should occur if he keeps checking his condition with the doctor and continues taking the prescribed medication.

Just as medication is prolonging the life of the stroke victim, advances in rehabilitation are increasing his chances of returning to a useful life. Doctors, therapists, and manufacturers have been devoting time and thought to these problems and are finding new answers almost daily, some of which have already been mentioned. A more detailed report will be given in the next chapter.

Even if the patient is in a wheel chair, there is no reason why he cannot follow many of his former pursuits. He can go to the movies or theater, engage in some outdoor games such as ping pong, pitching horseshoes, and swimming; and do most all household chores. He can play card games and dominoes and often can relearn scrabble and chess. In ping pong, if the opponent wants to equalize the odds, he can try sitting on a chair while playing. He may be surprised by the scores.

The patient who can walk, with or without a cane, can participate in all of these activities and more. He can take long walks, do gardening, or take up dancing— though he may not become a second Fred Astaire.

Almost all patients, in a wheel chair or not, can look

forward to a full and satisfactory sex life. While this may involve some understanding from the partner, this shouldn't be too much of a problem. Under the best of circumstances there has to be considerable understanding between the partners or there will be sexual problems.

As soon as the patient knows that he is making some progress with speech, walking and social activities, one question more will plague him. Will he be able to return to gainful employment?

For at least 40 per cent of the patients, perhaps even more now, the answer will be definitely yes. I have no doubt that this percentage will increase in the future.

Whether the patient will be able to return to the same job he held before the stroke is something that cannot be answered in general terms. It depends greatly on what he did before. If he was a salesman or a television announcer, it is doubtful that he can continue, since speech is so important. If his former job required the full use of both hands, this too is probably out of the question. Where the work was primarily done with one hand he may very well be able to go back to it. An example of this is the surgeon, mentioned in an earlier chapter, who learned to perform operations as well with his left hand as formerly with his right.

The person who finds that he can't return to his job or profession may at first feel that he's reached a dead-end street, but this isn't so. There is no reason why he can't learn a new vocation and support his family.

I have already mentioned the rehabilitation centers

and vocational rehabilitation offices that exist in every state. These centers specialize in occupational therapy and the teaching of new skills. As a result of their activities thousands of disabled people are now gainfully employed. More and more employers are realizing that many disabled people are still useful citizens and are opening their doors to them.

For complete information about where such training and guidance can be obtained, write to the National Society for Crippled Children and Adults, Inc., 2023 West Ogden Avenue, Chicago 12, Illinois.

19. Help

Throughout this book I have stressed the importance of the patient's being able to do things for himself. The more he can do for himself the more he will gratefully accept help in those things which are impossible. Where he can, the patient should learn to do things without mechanical aids. If, however, there are some things he can't manage, a device of some sort is preferable to being dependent on another person to do it for him.

Such aids as wheel chairs and crutches have been common for a long time, but not many advances were made in other areas until fairly recently. The first breakthrough was accomplished when the Institute of Physical Medicine and Rehabilitation, with a grant from the National Foundation for Infantile Paralysis, made a thorough study of the subject. They collected information from every possible source and in the process of the survey developed many ideas themselves, with the result that there are now many self-help devices on the market and more are appearing constantly. However, one problem remains. The patient who lives in a small community, or is unable to have professional therapy for other reasons, may not have the opportunity of learning about them.

Stroke victims are afflicted with so many kinds of disability that a device for one patient will not quite do for another. Many such devices, of course, can be adapted by someone even slightly handy with tools; or, once the basic idea is grasped, special aids can easily be made for the patient. Light, strong materials, such as aluminum or plastic, or even light wood, should be used.

First, let's consider the problems facing the patient who must use a wheel chair. Even if his condition is not permanent, he will face many situations which are difficult to solve while he is confined to the chair. Among the foremost is that doors are often simply too narrow to permit the passage of a wheel chair. This can be solved by getting a device which can be fixed to any folding wheel chair and is used to make the chair fold just enough to pass through narrow doorways. This is done with a lever that can be operated with one hand. Attaching it is simple enough so that it can be done by any member of the family. It is sold by Arnold Devices, Inc., 383 First Avenue, New York, N.Y.

The person in a wheel chair may have more difficulty in the bathroom than anywhere else. If there is a stall shower a chair can be placed in it, near the door, and the patient can transfer himself to it from the wheel chair. If a tub is used, the best device is either hand rails or a seat, or both. The patient may have considerable difficulty sitting on the bottom of the tub, especially if one arm is handicapped; a seat will make it much easier. If he can get that far, there is a very light seat that wedges in the tub about halfway down. This can be obtained from Lewis & Conger, 1980 Northern Boulevard, Manhassett, Long Island, N.Y.

When the patient needs to sit higher, two methods can be used. Place a chair or short stool, with rubber crutch tips on the legs, in the tub; or place a board at one end across the top of the tub. A ready-made board can be purchased, or one can be made at home. It can be made so that it fastens to the wall with a hinge, lifting up when not in use, or with attachments to prevent sliding.

Washing may be difficult for the stroke victim since one arm is nearly always paralyzed to some degree. Long-handled brushes are available which can be used for washing the back. A washcloth may prove difficult, especially in soaping. Mitts are available, made of toweling, with elastic around the top, which makes it much easier to use. Anyone good at sewing can make such a mitt. With a loop it can be hung within convenient reach on the wall next to the tub, so that the patient is able to slip his hand into it without assistance.

Where the patient finds it necessary to sit level with the top of the tub, a regular tub bath may not be practical. An inexpensive hand shower, which attaches to the water faucet, can be bought in any department or variety store, and the patient can with one hand direct the nozzle to all parts of his body.

While we're still in the bathroom, either the chair patient or the ambulant patient may find the toilet seat too low. A chair or low bench can be used with an opening cut in it to correspond with the toilet seat. In a home owned by the family, the toilet can be raised to the desired height with a strip of wood.

Many small things can be done in the bathroom to make it more convenient, and these can be worked out according to the patient's needs. A little thought and work can accomplish such tasks at hardly any expense.

The stroke victim may have difficulty washing his good hand or keeping his nails clean. A regular hand brush may be bought, to which suction cups are attached so that it can be placed on the wall, bristles facing outward.

The male patient may want to continue using a safety razor in shaving. If it's his right arm that's disabled he should be able to learn to use his left. If his right arm is only partially disabled but he has trouble holding the razor, attachments can be had which will hold it to his hand. I would suggest, however, if his medication includes anticoagulants, that he stick to an electric razor.

The wheel-chair patient will need a mirror hung at his level and at least one shelf for shaving equipment and other toilet articles.

While the wheel chair will fit under most tables and desks, the patient may want something more convenient for writing and reading, since it is difficult to handle a book with one hand. A combination writing board and reading rack can be built to attach to the arms of the wheel chair. When used for writing it is a plain piece of board. But by cutting it in two and fastening them together with hinges, one part can be raised to serve as a reading rack. When raised it can be held in place by metal strips on either side or by a notched support in the back. It can be built with no more tools than a saw and a screwdriver. If the person who intends making it is not handy with tools, he can consult his local hardware store about the pieces he will require.

In using the reading rack, the stroke victim will need an addition if he has the use of only one arm. There are many ways of holding the pages of the book down while he is reading but probably one of the best, and certainly the least expensive, is two strips of elastic around the rack so that when the book is opened each side will fit under one strip. Thus the book pages are held down. When the second page is read, it can be pulled from beneath one elastic and slipped in under the other.

There is also a tray and reading rack, which can be used for such other things as typing, manufactured in New York. It can be secured from Adjustics, Inc., 169 Thompson St., New York. In writing to any of these companies for information, ask for a catalogue, since it is impossible for me to list all the things available.

Wheel chairs have been greatly improved in the past few years. The old, heavy chair has vanished to be replaced by a much lighter chair in a variety of models. Since they are relatively expensive, the patient should be sure to get the advice of his physician about the model he should buy. There are not only differences in size but in types of back and foot rests, and one kind may be better for the patient than another. A custom-built wheel chair can be had by those who can afford it.

Where only a few steps lead from the house to the street level, a ramp can easily be constructed from two-by-fours and one-inch pine. Cut off part of the two-by-fours at the bottom so they will rest squarely on the ground and cut a notch where they touch the top step, so that the ramp will not slip. This will provide a much easier way for the chair to be taken in and out of the house while the patient is in it. If the ramp is not too steep he may be able to manage it himself.

Either the patient or a member of the family should make certain the chair is well cared for. Most manufacturers provide instructions on the care and lubrication; such directions should be carefully followed.

In getting a chair for the stroke victim with a paralyzed arm, the family should be certain to get a one-arm drive so that he can get around by himself. Be sure that the chair has brakes and that the lever is on the side of the patient's good arm. The small front wheels on chairs usually come in two sizes; the larger size is generally better for getting over obstacles.

I've already written about special methods in the kitchen and given the sources of more information. Considerable research has been done on the subject, for the number of physically handicapped women in the nation is up in the millions. One of the basic necessities, however, is the reorganization of the kitchen. Utensils and supplies should be arranged for the convenience of the wheel-

chair patient, and if possible there should be some re-
modeling, with china closets and so on placed at a better
level. Most sinks can be lowered for easier dishwashing.
Ironing boards with shorter legs can be bought, or someone in the family can shorten the legs on the old one.

The homemaker who is confined to a chair may also
find difficulty with the refrigerator. Sometimes this can
be solved by rearranging the things on the shelves, but
there are many refrigerators on the market today that
go a long way toward solving the problem. Such things
as automatic defrost, a vertical freezer unit, and revolv-
ing shelves are valuable aids.

If the cooking range is checked, it probably can be
easily lowered. Many stoves are made so that they can
be lowered or raised. Stoves are usually too high for the
person in a chair, but if lowered just a few inches they
can be used with no trouble at all.

If the patient lives in the New York City area, the Institute of Physical Medicine and Rehabilitation has a
model kitchen where its therapy patients are trained
and which can also be a guide to fixing up the home
kitchen. If the patient lives elsewhere, valuable information can be obtained from the Institute.

The furniture in the home should be arranged so that
there is plenty of room for the wheel chair. Small throw
rugs should be avoided as they may cause the chair to
skid. Where there are no rugs on the flors, a nonskid wax
should always be used. Everything in the home should
be re-evaluated with the patient in mind. His bed, for
example, should be placed on blocks to raise it to about

the same height as his chair. This will make it much easier for him to transfer between the bed and chair without assistance.

If the homemaker was formerly fond of embroidering or knitting there is no reason why she can't resume it, even though she has complete use of only one hand and may be in a wheel chair. There are devices which allow either of these crafts to be done one-handed. Most are made in Europe but they can be found here. If the therapist doesn't know where, information can be obtained at the Institute of Physical Medicine and Rehabilitation. Or else a member of the family handy with tools can work out something to serve the purpose.

A small but frustrating problem for the wheel-chair patient occurs when things are dropped on the floor. Leaning over too far may be too hard, or he may be afraid of tipping the chair. A pair of long-handled tongs, that can be operated with one hand, will make it easier to recover such objects.

Doctors and therapists have discovered that one of the most important activities for the physically disabled is that of feeding themselves. Many have commented on the fact that the food does not taste the same when it is fed to them. When possible, the patient should learn to use his right hand. This may be difficult at first. Since the grip will be weak in the disabled hand, there is the problem of holding the fork, knife, and spoon firmly enough so that the food will not be spilled or the utensil will not fall. Several types of handles are available, ranging from those with grooves to fit the fingers, and handles

with the metal looped so the whole hand can be thrust
through it (similar to many baby spoons), to large plastic
handles which can be strapped onto the hand, developed by the National Silver Company, the Veterans
Administration Hospital in Virginia, and the Institute of
Physical Medicine and Rehabilitation.

The Institute also has other models which can be
easily made at home by using elastic to fit around the
hand and a pocket for the handle made of leather or
other strong durable material. Information about this
and other devices can be had from the Institute.

There is a combination fork-knife with a curved blade,
which is useful in cutting meat with one hand since it
can be done with a rocking motion that does not require
holding the meat with a fork in the other hand. It is
made by the Winkley Artificial Limb Co., 90 Fifth Avenue, New York, N.Y., or Lamson & Goodnow Mfg. Co.,
Shelburne Falls, Mass.

I've already mentioned several uses for double-suction
cups. These can also be used by the one-handed eater to
hold a soup bowl on the table.

I have also mentioned a number of aids in dressing,
especially for men, but there are many others besides.
Full information on others can be had from the sources
I've listed.

During the period before the woman patient has recovered the use of the limbs, she may find that maternity
clothes are better than regular clothes. The looser fit
makes them easier to put on and take off. Maternity slacks

are made with zippers on both legs and thus are more convenient for the disabled leg.

Women may also have trouble with stockings. There is a device, consisting of a handle and specially shaped wire at one end, which will slip inside a rolled stocking once it is on the foot and, when pulled on, unrolls the stocking up the leg. (More information on this can be obtained from the Rehabilitation Services, Inc., Binghampton, N.Y.) If there is difficulty in getting the stocking on the foot, a long-handled shoe horn may help.

The problems faced by the person limited to the use of one arm are so many they'd fill several books—if one person could think of all of them, since they vary with each individual. Most of them will seem small and unimportant until the patient is faced with them. Then they will loom larger than a mountain. One that confronts the patient with glasses is how to clean them.

A simple aid can be built at home without much trouble or cost. Fasten two clothes pins, of the snap variety, to a plain board, positioned so that they can hold the earpieces of the glasses. They can then be cleaned easily. A more complex device, and probably better in performance, has been developed. Information on this can be obtained from the Occupational Therapy Department, Veterans Administration Center, Los Angeles, California.

The same department has developed a device to be used by the patient for trimming the nails on his good hand. A nail clipper is fastened to a board or table, and is equipped with a wire and a loop of leather so that it can be operated by the foot.

The patient may have difficulty in using the telephone, especially if it becomes necessary for him to copy down information while listening. There are many methods for solving this, designed for those who are seriously handicapped, but there is a simple and easily available one for the average stroke victim. Known as the Telerest, it is a device which clamps onto the receiver and fits over the shoulder, holding the phone to the ear. Thus the good hand is free for dialing or writing. This can be purchased in almost any department store and is inexpensive.

If the patient wants to use a typewriter, perhaps as a means of earning a living, there is no reason why he can't do so despite the disability of one arm. A special keyboard has been devised with the keys arranged for the convenience of the one-handed typist. Information on this can be had from the Tytell Typewriting Company, Inc., 123 Fulton Street, New York, N.Y.

A final word on self-help devices. While various therapy centers have done much valuable work in this area, much has been contributed by patients themselves. For that reason the patient need not rely on what has been done. It may be that not all of them will work for his individual problems and he certainly shouldn't try to use an aid that isn't right for him. On the other hand, the patient, a member of his family, or a friend may be able to work out an improvement—which can also be passed on to others.

Whenever such new devices are developed by the pa-

206

tient or his family, a description should be sent to an organization such as the Institute of Physical Medicine and Rehabilitation, so that their general use can be evaluated and passed on. The patient may not make any money from such an idea but he will have the satisfaction of helping others as well as himself.

Remember that a determination to improve in every way possible is a basic factor in the stroke patient's progress. It will be the basic factor in how much of a normal life he can achieve. With a strong enough will, he cannot be prevented by not being able to find the exact self-help aid he needs. He'll invent his own.

20. The Short History of a Long Story

This has been largely a personal book—even those sections devoted to general information. Looking back on it, it seems to me that I have lived every part of it, although much of it did not actually happen to me.

In a new way, I did live it all. First, I shared an experience with several million people—without being immediately aware of it. Like each of them, at the time I felt completely alone, as if this were something that had never happened to anybody in the world except myself. I didn't actually understand what had happened to me but I knew it was terrible and I could see no reason why it should have happened. And I shared with others—as I later learned—a firm belief that the doctors would soon give me a pill or a shot that would make me well again. Or maybe nature would take care of it. I wasn't sure about the method, only about the result.

Then came the day, which I've already described,

when I realized that none of this was true, that I was going to be handicapped to some degree for the rest of my life—what degree of disability would be up to me alone. Others could help me but I'd have to do it myself. For a short time I was overcome with self-pity and a sense of futility. It was too big a job. I couldn't do it. I didn't know it then, but this, too, I shared with millions of others.

At last the day came when I faced the issue squarely and determined that somehow I would do it. I would find a way to take care of myself, at least do some of the things I had always enjoyed, and become a useful and self-sustaining citizen again. I also learned later that this was an experience not necessarily shared by all of us who have experienced a stroke. Many never get beyond the period of depression and futility. There is no valid reason for this. Given understanding and some form of professional help they should go far beyond that stage.

Once I decided that I did have a future, I became intensely interested in the subject of strokes. I read everything I could find. My wife, my sisters, and my daughter were alerted to bring me anything on the subject they chanced upon. I kept a file of clippings on strokes from newspapers and magazines. I kept as accurate a record as I could on my own progress. Later, while working on this book, I was to talk to many doctors and therapists.

Two important things came out of this. I acquired a fairly good knowledge of the subject and its meaning, not only to stroke patients but to society as a whole. I learned the varying differences among patients—from those confined, speechless and helpless, to a bed, to those able to go back to a job or profession. Regardless of differences, we were all related in that we faced the same problems within ourselves and in going out into the world. I think that this knowledge greatly contributed to my own progress. I know that it developed my insight into my own problems and gave me an awareness of the two choices available to me—to go ahead or slip back.

Secondly, it gave me many a direct answer to things I was trying to solve. For example, it was a book then published only in England, *Stroke*, by Douglas Ritchie, that first taught me how to tie my shoelaces one-handed. I have since learned that two other methods are taught here, but then I was having considerable trouble with that problem. I learned other things from other books; certainly something valuable was in every one that I read.

In a way, I was fortunate. I lived in New York City when I had my stroke, a city that probably has more doctors, therapists, and hospitals devoted to this and similar illnesses than any other. I had a good doctor. I had physical therapy beginning in the hospital and speech therapy soon after leaving it. I was in a fine hospital and then was tested at St. Barnabas, one of the best rehabilitation hospitals in the country. I managed to read everything on the subject that my family and I could find. In spite of this, there was much information available that I missed because I did not know where to look for it.

The idea of writing a book about my own personal experiences occurred to me early in my rehabilitation. At first, I merely thought that the story of what I was going through could give help and encouragement to others and their families. But as I acquired additional information I came to realize that there were many persons whose problems differed enough to require more than that. I began to see the book as a complete (as much so as I could make it) guide to living through a stroke and recovering from it. My own experience would be valuable, but so would the accumulated information that was scattered through dozens of books, pamphlets, brochures, and monographs.

It should be a book, I thought, that would give the stroke victim, and his family, an understanding of his illness and the awareness that considerable recovery was not impossible. It should provide vital information about therapy and rehabilitation for those who were isolated geographically from the best sources. It also should give the reader basic facts about self-help methods and aids and tell him where and how to get more detailed information. This, and the idea for the Foundation, became two of my most important projects for the future long before I had recovered enough to tackle them.

Throughout the book I have listed essential pamphlets on various aspects of rehabilitation and where they can be secured. There are also a number of books which provide valuable information. Some may repeat things to be found elsewhere, but they are all worth reading.

Stroke: A Study of Recovery, Douglas Ritchie. New York: Doubleday, 1961.

As far as I know, this is the only other book written by someone who has had a stroke. It is mostly written in diary form, giving a running account of his experiences following the stroke.

Strokes: How They Occur and What Can Be Done About Them, Irvine S. Page, M.D., Clark M. Millikan, M.D., Irving S. Wright, M.D., Edward Weiss, M.D., E. Stanley Crawford, M.D., Michael E. De Bakey, M.D., and Howard A. Rusk, M.D. New York: E. P. Dutton, 1961.

While fairly technical, this book, each section written by a specialist, gives a fairly rounded picture.

New Hope for Stroke Victims, Robert A. Kuhn, M.D., New York: Appleton-Century-Crofts, 1960.

Dr. Kuhn is a neurosurgeon and one of the pioneers in the new field of angiography, with which the book is mostly concerned.

Living With a Disability, Howard A. Rusk, M.D., and Eugene J. Taylor, in collaboration with Muriel Zimmerman, O.T.R. and Julia Judson, M.S. New York: Blakiston (McGraw-Hill), 1953.

This is probably one of the most complete books published to date on aids for the physically handicapped, with almost three hundred photographs. It is not limited to the rehabilitation of stroke patients and should be valuable to any family where there is a handicapped person.

Physical Rehabilitation for Daily Living, Edith Buch-
wald. New York: McGraw-Hill, 1952.
   Another valuable guide to the everyday problems of
   the person with a disability.

New Hope for the Handicapped, Howard A. Rusk, M.D.,
and Eugene J. Taylor. New York: Harper and Row, 1949.
   Although this book was published in 1949 there are
   still many worthwhile things in it. Dr. Rusk heads the
   Institute of Physical Medicine and Rehabilitation and
   is one of the outstanding leaders in rehabilitation.

Normal Lives for the Disabled, Edna Yost. New York:
Macmillan, 1944.
   Another book published several years ago but still
   valuable.

Management in Daily Living, Ruth Bonde. New York:
Macmillan, 1944.

Management in Family Living, Paula Nickell and J. M.
Dorsey. New York: John Wiley & Sons, 1959.

Housekeeping Made Easy, Linda Marvin. New York:
Vanguard Press, 1943.
   The three books listed above are, of course, for the
   homemaker who has been disabled. They were published several years ago but are still up to date in much
   of their information.

Guide to Easier Living, Mary and Russell Wright. New
York: Simon & Schuster, 1950.
   This is a guide to home building as well as homemak-
   ing for those who are handicapped.

Now that more attention is being paid to those who have become handicapped as the result of illness, many more books will undoubtedly appear in the future. If the patient's local newspaper carries news of books he should watch it for any new publications.

I'm well aware that many families cannot afford to buy the books I have listed, especially when they also have the problem of caring for someone who has just recovered from a stroke. This, however, should not keep them from reading the books, and becoming familiar with all the problems and solutions that are presently known.

Almost every community today has a public library. The patient or a member of the family can take out a card at the library simply by asking for one. It is true that many small libraries, and perhaps even some fairly large ones, will not have these books on their shelves. But the various public libraries in the United States are roughly linked together and you will find that the local library can borrow books from the state library or the library of a nearby community. It is a free service to all who have cards, so that it should be possible to get most, if not all, of these books.

It is surprising how much information can be obtained if you try, and how much it will help the person who needs it most. The patient who is so armed has the best chance of winning his battle.

PART III

"The goal of every handicapped person is to achieve as great a degree as possible of independence—to do as much as possible for himself."

HOWARD A. RUSK, M.D.

Robert E. Van Rosen—1959-62

Although, as I have stated, the course of a stroke and the recovery from it are different for each person, readers may be interested in the time involved in my own. Since it is difficult to go through a book picking out the various stages, I include a brief schedule of what has happened to me. While it may not be the same as other patients' experiences, it can still offer some encouragement to those who are uncertain of what they are facing. It should be remembered, however, that in many respects my progress was faster than the average.

I've already told the background to my stroke, the thrombophlebitis which finally resulted in a pulmonary embolism and my operation. This started in the spring of 1953; at the end of two years I had almost completely recovered except that I still had to wear elastic stockings and keep my legs elevated several hours each day. I was being given medication for high blood pressure but otherwise I felt fine. This continued for another four years when the present story started.

April, 1959	I began to feel a slight numbness in my right arm. It would last only a few minutes and there were long intervals between the attacks.
May, 1959	I was still having the occasional numbness in my right arm so I went to see my doctor. He examined me and then sent me to a neurologist. I was admitted to the hospital and given a thorough examination, including an electroencephalogram.
June 7, 1959	I was given a clean bill of health by the specialist.
June 13, 1959	Marcia and I went to Connecticut for the day. For the first time I was unable to use my right arm when I tried to feed myself at lunch and again at dinner. I began to have some speech difficulty on the way home. On arriving there about midnight, I phoned my doctor. He came to the apartment and examined me. He thought it might be a stroke and ordered me to the hospital at once. I was admitted that night.
June 14, 1959	Although I still had the same difficulties I had experienced the night before, I still thought it was nothing serious and was trying to conduct my business from the hospital by phone.
June 17, 1959	My condition became much worse.

There is still some question as to whether I had a second stroke or the first one merely became worse.

June 20, 1959   By this time I was running a very high temperature and the paralysis had extended from my right arm to my right leg. For the next ten days they were not sure whether I would live or not.

July 2, 1959   My stroke was completed and I began my physical therapy.

July 31, 1959   I came home from the hospital. I was still getting physical therapy, Mr. Melniker coming to my apartment every day. In the days immediately following my homecoming, I started reading and writing with the aid of my wife.

Sept. 15, 1959   I tried speech therapy with a professional but didn't feel it was going well so I discontinued it after the second session and went back to working with my wife.

Nov. 13, 1959   Still continuing physical therapy. I also went to Dr. Laszewski for general tests and evaluation, the results of which I have already reported. It was also in this period that I tried hypnosis.

Jan. 7, 1960   I went to Hunter College where I was examined in the speech clinic.

Feb. 4, 1960   I started with speech therapy at Hunter College, going three times a week. This was much better than my first experience with a professional therapist and I began to feel that I was making progress.

March 1, 1960 This was when I tried the treatment of H3 injections. It was also during this period, or earlier, that I decided I was improved enough to try to go back to work and my sister and I started promoting my machine. As I've stated, it was a period full of endless frustrations.

May 1960 We were not having too much success with selling the machine and so I rented part of the office to another business.

Aug. 1, 1960 Gave up the business and moved out of the office.

Sept. 1, 1960 I had improved enough so that my medication no longer included narcotics.

Oct. 15, 1960 The people who were interested in my machine showed up and I made my deal with them.

Nov. 1, 1960 This was a big day for me. I had seemed to make enough progress to discontinue both the physical and the speech therapy. I was even able to use my right hand to feed myself. I felt more optimistic than I had at any time since the stroke.

March 17, 1961 My machine was supposed to be taken to Chicago for an industrial exhibit and I was supposed to go along. At this point, I began to have trouble with my new partners and once again I was in a constant state of irritation. Suddenly my right leg became paralyzed again, so badly that I had to resort to a wheel chair. There is some medical disagreement as to whether I merely had a setback or had suffered a "little" stroke. I finally reached an agreement with my partners and the machine went off to Chicago without me.

March 30, 1961 I was sent back to the hospital for an intense anticoagulant treatment, supplemented with Vitamin K. I was there for a week and was then sent home, feeling much better.

May 15, 1961 Marcia went to Europe for a short vacation. I had decided it would be too much of a trip for me but that I would go to the country for a few weeks. I was able to get around fine and to look after myself. I was there less than two weeks when something developed in the scar of my old operation. I called my doctor in New York City and he suggested that I return. When I got there he discovered that I had a blood clot in the scar. Back I went to the hospital for more anticoagulant treatments, staying another week.

June 1960 Marcia back from Europe.

July-Aug., 1960   This was a period of dramatic improvement in my condition. I recovered all the ground I had lost a few months earlier and began to move ahead once more in terms of physical and mental advances. From this time on my progress was consistent and without further setbacks.

Nov. 1, 1961   With the assistance of my sister Beatrice, I wrote the outline for my book. Throughout this period I was making constant progress in the physical things I could do and in my speech. I also began to straighten out the affairs of my corporation and to work on the idea for the Foundation.

Feb., 1962   The contract was signed for my book and I began to work on it.

April, 1962   This was when I was first able to climb the ladder on my terrace. Once this would have been a trivial accomplishment but by this time it was a major feat.

May, 1962   I returned to Dr. Laszewski for further testing and evaluation—with the results you have already read. The rest is up to me.